Electrochemistry

P. D. Groves

John Murray   Albemarle Street   London

Printed and bound in Hong Kong by
Wing King Tong Co Ltd

0 7195 2935 2

1986

Electrochemistry

MODERN CHEMISTRY BACKGROUND READERS

Edited by **J. G. Stark**
Head of Chemistry, Glasgow Academy

Other titles in the series:

The Shapes of Organic Molecules   *N. G. Clark*
Chemical Periodicity   *D. G. Cooper*
Inorganic Complexes   *D. Nicholls*

Preface

A distinguished electrochemist has called electrochemistry the 'under-developed science'. Although that description is perhaps less true today than it was when written in 1965, it still remains true that many of the potentialities of the subject have yet to be realized. Nevertheless, electrochemistry is an important branch of science and has contributed in many ways to our present understanding of the nature of matter. It has provided valuable tools for the scientific investigator and, in the industrial and technological fields, has given rise to developments on which much of our modern civilization depends. In the future electrochemistry can be expected to contribute even further to society's needs. The realization that the Earth's resources are finite must lead to an increased emphasis on the need to utilize these resources in such a way that wastage—and the associated pollution—are kept to a minimum. Electrochemical methods of producing industrial chemicals and energy, to take two examples, have many advantages in this respect over more conventional methods, even though much remains to be done before they can be fully exploited.

This book attempts to lay down the foundations of electrochemistry so that they are readily intelligible to the beginner and the non-specialist. The subject is developed in a way that is wholly consistent with modern concepts and is related where possible to present day industrial and technological developments.

Little previous knowledge is required apart from a basic familiarity with elementary chemistry. The approach is almost completely descriptive and there is little reference to the quantitative and mathematical aspects of the subject. This is not to say that these aspects are not important: clearly no science can exist without being contained within an adequate theoretical framework. Nevertheless, it is the author's view that an understanding of fundamental theory can best follow an appreciation of the observations and facts of the subject and that too early an attempt to force these into a mathematical form can discourage many able students from further interest and study.

It is hoped that this book will be found useful by many different groups of students. It covers the requirements for electrochemical topics in A-level syllabuses, although going beyond these in a number of important respects so that they may be seen in the broader context of the subject. First year college and university students should also find the book useful, not because it will be sufficient on its own, but because it provides a foundation from which they can go on to a better understanding of more comprehensive texts. Students of disciplines other than chemistry, whose work nevertheless requires some familiarity with electrochemical methods, should also find material of value to them.

The illustrations in this book have been prepared by Mrs Joyce Poole whose assistance is very gratefully acknowledged.

Peter Groves   *Birmingham* 1974

Contents

Introduction: Electrochemistry, Electricity, and Electrical Units   1

Electrochemistry is that branch of science which is concerned with the inter-relationship of electricity and chemistry, the close affinity of these subjects having first become clear from Faraday's studies of electrolysis published in 1833 and 1834. Electrochemistry deals, firstly, with the nature and properties of substances containing charged particles known as ions and, secondly, with the relationships between chemical reactions and electric currents. These divisions are sometimes known as *ionics* and *electrodics* respectively. Ionics is dealt with in Chapters 2 to 6 of this book and electrodics in Chapters 7 to 10. In the last two chapters some modern industrial and technological applications of the subject are discussed.

As is now well known, all matter is electrical in nature. The atoms of which substances are composed each consist of a nucleus which carries a positive electrical charge surrounded by electrons which carry a negative electrical charge. In a simple atom the amount of positive charge on the nucleus is exactly balanced by the amount of negative charge on the surrounding electrons. Such an atom is electrically neutral. Similarly, in a simple molecule the total amount of positive charge on the nuclei of the component atoms is balanced by the total amount of negative charge on all the electrons in the molecule.

It is possible to disturb the balance of electrical charges in atoms and molecules in various ways. When certain materials are rubbed together, for example amber and silk, some electrons are transferred from the surface molecules of one substance to the surface of the other. This gives rise to the phenomenon of static electricity. The effect is made use of in the Wimshurst machine which can generate large amounts of electricity. In certain weather conditions a somewhat similar process causes the build-up of static charge on clouds, the discharge of which produces thunder and lightning.

The presence of a static charge causes bodies to attract or repel one another. Although the existence of static electricity was known to the ancient Greeks the first systematic study of it was made by Coulomb (1736–1806). He formulated the law, now known as Coulomb's law, which states that the force of attraction or repulsion F between two electrical charges Q_1 and Q_2 in a vacuum at a distance l apart is given by

$$F = k \frac{Q_1 Q_2}{l^2} \qquad (1.1)$$

where k is a constant. When one of the charges is positive and the other negative the force is an attraction; when the charges are both positive or both negative the force is a repulsion. Such forces are known as *electrostatic* or *coulombic* forces.

When the charges are contained within a medium—for example, a liquid—the equation becomes

$$F = k \frac{Q_1 Q_2}{\varepsilon_r l^2} \tag{1.2}$$

where ε_r is known as the *dielectric constant* (or relative permittivity) of the medium. For air and many gases ε_r is approximately equal to one. For many liquids it has values not very much greater than one (table 1). For certain liquids, however, much larger values are observed. One important liquid, water, has a dielectric constant of nearly 80. This means that two electric charges immersed in water attract or repel each other with a force approximately one-eightieth of what it would be in a vacuum. This has some important consequences as we shall see later. The unit with which we measure the amount of electric charge is known as the *coulomb*, C. The amount of electric charge possessed by one electron equals 1.602×10^{-19} C.

When electric charge passes from one point to another we say that an *electric current* is flowing. Current is measured in terms of the number of coulombs flowing per second, one coulomb per second being known as one *ampere*, A.

Before an electric current can flow between two points they must be electrically charged to different extents. The level of electric charge is known as the *electric potential*: a current may flow when there is a *potential difference* between the two points. The magnitude of the current flowing depends on two factors: the potential difference and the *resistance* between the points. The unit of potential difference is the *volt*, V, and the unit of resistance is the *ohm*, Ω. The relationship between potential

Liquid	Dielectric constant (temperature/°C in brackets)
Hexane	1.89 (20)
1,4-Dioxan	2.21 (25)
Tetrachloromethane	2.24 (20)
Benzene	2.28 (20)
Ethoxyethane (ether)	4.34 (20)
Toluene	4.38 (25)
Trichloromethane	4.81 (20)
Propanone	20.70 (25)
Ammonia (liquid)	22 (−33.4)
Water	78.54 (25)
Sulphuric acid	110 (20)
Methanamide	109 (25)

Table 1 Dielectric constants of some liquids.

difference, V, current flowing, I, and resistance, R, is given by Ohm's law:

$$V = IR \tag{1.3}$$

The resistances of various materials vary between wide limits. Some materials (for example gases, some liquids, ceramics) have extremely high resistances and are known as *insulators*; other materials (such as graphite and many metals) have low resistances and are known as *conductors*. The actual resistance of a particular material depends upon its shape: a short thick wire will have a lower resistance than a long thin wire of the same metal even though the actual amounts of metal are the same in both wires. Consequently, it is usual to characterize different substances by their *resistivities*, this quantity being a constant for a given substance. For a cylinder of length l and cross-sectional area A the resistivity ρ is defined as

$$\rho = \frac{RA}{l} \tag{1.4}$$

We can rearrange this equation to

$$R = \frac{\rho l}{A}$$

which shows that the resistance of a wire is directly proportional to its length and inversely proportional to its cross-sectional area: this is, of course, what we would expect.

Substance	Resistivity/ Ωcm (temperature/°C in brackets)
Silver	1.59×10^{-6} (20)
Copper	1.69×10^{-6} (20)
Aluminium	2.83×10^{-6} (20)
Mercury	9.58×10^{-5} (20)
Antimony	4.17×10^{-5} (20)
Lead	2.2×10^{-5} (20)
Graphite	8.00×10^{-4} (20)
Calcium chloride (melt)	8.6×10^{-1} (750)
Potassium chloride (0.01 M)	7.83×10^{2} (20)
Water	1×10^{6} (20)
Sulphur	8×10^{15} (17)
Rubber	1×10^{18} (22)

Table 2 Resistivities of some substances.

Certain chemical substances dissolve in water and other solvents to produce solutions which are electrically conducting. Instead of referring to the resistance and resistivity of these solutions we prefer to use the terms *conductance* and *conductivity*. The conductance G is the reciprocal of the resistance and the conductivity κ the reciprocal of the resistivity:

$$G = 1/R \quad \kappa = 1/\rho \tag{1.5}$$

Conductances are measured in the reciprocal unit, Ω^{-1}: this is also known as the siemens, S $(= \Omega^{-1})$. Some conductivities of potassium chloride solutions are given in table 3.

Concentration of solution	Conductivity/Ω^{-1} cm^{-1}
1 M	1.0207×10^{-1}
0.1 M	1.167×10^{-2}
0.01 M	1.278×10^{-3}

Table 3 Conductivity of aqueous potassium chloride solutions (at 20 °C).

Chemical Bonds and Chemical Reactions 2

The properties of matter are intimately related to its *structure*, particularly to the structure of the atoms and molecules of which all matter is composed. Chemical reactions always involve a *change of structure* and the electrochemist is interested in those reactions, and in the corresponding changes of structure, which are related to observable electrical effects; for example, chemical reactions produced by electric currents, and electric currents produced by chemical reactions.

The structural changes are primarily due to changes in chemical bonds, an understanding of which is essential not only for the electrochemist but for the student of any branch of chemistry. There are several different types of chemical bond and hence several different principal classes of chemical compounds.

Ionic compounds

When the elements sodium and fluorine react together there is a transfer of electrons between the sodium atoms and the fluorine atoms, each sodium atom losing an electron and each fluorine atom gaining an electron:*

$$Na \rightarrow Na^+ + e^- \qquad F + e^- \rightarrow F^-$$

The sodium and fluorine atoms which have lost or gained electrons are

---

*The reaction is, in fact, rather more complex than this for, unless carried out at high temperatures, the two elements do not exist as separated atoms. At ordinary temperatures fluorine exists as F_2 molecules and sodium as a solid in which the atoms are linked by means of the metallic bond. The reaction must, therefore, also involve the breaking of these bonds.

known as *ions*, the sodium ion being positively charged and the fluorine ion negatively charged. Sodium fluoride then is an example of an *ionic compound* or *salt*. The resultant ions interact electrically in a very complex way, all the ions of like charge repelling each other, and all the ions of unlike charge attracting each other. At ordinary temperatures the resulting balance of electric forces produces a crystal of sodium fluoride (figure 1) in which each sodium ion is surrounded by six fluoride ions while each fluoride ion is surrounded by six sodium ions. There is very little neutralization of charge between adjacent Na^+ and F^- ions and we can assume that the crystal is made up of separate and, in a sense, independent ions.

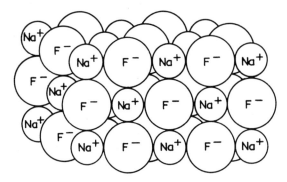

Figure 1 The structure of a crystal of sodium fluoride.

In terms of atomic and molecular orbitals, we can say that in this reaction there has been a complete transfer of electrons from the atomic orbitals of the sodium atoms to the atomic orbitals of the fluorine atoms. There is very little interaction between adjacent atomic orbitals on the two different atoms and consequently no formation of molecular orbitals.

Polar compounds

If we substitute hydrogen for sodium in the above reaction with fluorine, a far less complete transfer of electrons takes place. In this case, atomic orbitals on the hydrogen and the fluorine atoms combine together to form a molecular orbital: in other words, a molecule of hydrogen fluoride is formed in which the two atoms are linked by means of a *covalent bond*. However, electrons are still attracted more towards the fluorine atom than they are towards the hydrogen atom and in consequence the hydrogen atom carries a *partial* positive charge while the fluorine atom carries a *partial* negative charge. Such a molecule is said to be a *dipole*. It can be written as

$$H^{\delta+}—F^{\delta-}$$

where δ is some fraction less than one. (If it were equal to one hydrogen fluoride would be an ionic substance like sodium fluoride.) A substance whose molecules have this kind of structure is said to be a *polar* substance.

Electronegativity and chemical bonding

Elements like fluorine which are capable of taking up electrons are known as *electronegative* elements: elements like sodium and hydrogen which tend to lose electrons are known as *electropositive* elements.

It is convenient to draw up a table which expresses the degree of *electronegativity* of each element in the periodic table. A part of the electronegativity table due to Linus Pauling is shown in table 4. In this table the larger numbers indicate the strongly electronegative elements and the smaller numbers the electropositive elements. Note the intermediate position of hydrogen, and also that fluorine is the most electronegative element known.

The ionic bond

When two elements, one of which is strongly electronegative and the other strongly electropositive, react, more or less complete electron transfer takes place between the atoms (as in the case of sodium fluoride). The resulting compound is an ionic compound and the bonding between its ions is known as *ionic bonding*.

The covalent bond

When elements which do not differ so greatly in their electronegativities react, two possibilities arise. If the two elements both have a fair degree of electronegative character, bonding takes place by a *sharing* of electrons. One or more pairs of atomic orbitals on the two atoms combine together to form one or more molecular orbitals. The resulting compound is a covalent compound and the chemical bonds between its atoms are known as *covalent bonds*. Molecules of the compound are formed (as in H_2, N_2, CH_4, H_2S, for example) in contrast to the situation in an ionic compound where only separate ions are found.

	Li	Be						
	0.98	1.57						
	Na	Mg						
Table 4	0.93	1.31						
Electronegativities of	K	Ca	Sc	Ti	V	Cr	Mn	Fe
some elements.	0.82	1.00	1.36	1.54	1.63	1.66	1.55	1.83

The metallic bond

The other possibility arises when the elements are of low electronegativity, that is, in the case of the metallic elements. Let us consider first the simplest situation where all the atoms are of the same sort, for example in the metal copper. Within a crystal of this metal the atoms are packed together in what is known as a *close-packed structure*. (This is the sort of structure obtained when spheres are packed together as closely as they will go.) Because the atoms are in such close contact there is an interaction between the atomic orbitals of a given atom and the atomic orbitals of *all* of its immediate neighbours (twelve in number). Each neighbour in turn interacts in the same way with all of its neighbours. These interactions are similar to those which give molecular orbitals in covalent compounds. However, in this case the orbitals are not localized between pairs of atoms but extend throughout the whole of the crystal and embrace all of the atoms within it. The electrons within these bonds can then move more or less freely throughout the crystal: this is responsible for many of the characteristic properties of the metals, notably the fact that they conduct electricity. This type of bonding is known as *metallic bonding*.

The metallic bond can also be formed between different metals: in this case the resultant compound is known as an *alloy*. Copper and zinc, for example, bond in this way to form the alloy known as brass.

A simple way of picturing a metal is as a collection of close-packed positive ions in a sea of electrons, the electrons being able to move more or less freely between the ions. The detailed nature of the bonding (the study of which is beyond the scope of this text) determines just how free this movement is and consequently determines the actual electrical resistance of the metal.

Giant molecules and layer structures

Some elements (for example, hydrogen, oxygen, nitrogen, sulphur, phosphorus) normally exist in the pure state as small molecules (H_2, O_2, N_2, S_8, P_4). Some other elements, however, form what are known as *giant molecules*. In diamond, for example, each carbon atom is joined by covalent bonds to four other carbon atoms: these in turn are each joined to four carbon atoms, the linkage extending throughout the whole of the

			H 2.20			
			B 2.04	**C** 2.55	**N** 3.04	**O** 3.44	**F** 3.98
			Al 1.61	**Si** 1.90	**P** 2.19	**S** 2.58	**Cl** 3.16
Ni 1.91	**Cu** 1.90	**Zn** 1.65	**Ga** 1.81	**Ge** 2.01	**As** 2.18	**Se** 2.55	**Br** 2.96

crystal (figure 2). The only boundaries to the bonding are the faces of the crystal—hence the use of the term giant molecule to describe the structure. Although there is some superficial resemblance to metallic bonding the situation is quite different in that all the bonds are firmly localized between adjacent carbon atoms. Electrons, therefore, cannot move throughout the crystal and, in consequence, diamond is an electrical insulator.

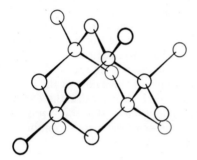

Figure 2 The structure of diamond. Each carbon atom is linked to four other carbon atoms, the linkage extending throughout the whole of the crystal.

Silicon and germanium, being elements of group IV, have this same type of giant molecular structure. These elements, however, have more electrons than carbon has and there is, superimposed on the strictly localized covalent bonding, a more generalized type of metal-like bonding. These elements have, in consequence, a very small electrical conductivity and are known as *semiconductors*. They have very characteristic electrical properties and play an important part in some areas of modern technology.

Although diamond is an insulator, the other allotrope of carbon, graphite, has an appreciable electrical conductivity. This substance has a quite different type of structure in which the carbon atoms are arranged in sheets or layers (figure 3). Only three of the four valence electrons of each atom are involved in the formation of covalent bonds between adjacent atoms: the remaining electron takes part in a type of bonding which is more akin to metallic bonding. This bonding however does not extend throughout the crystal but is localized between the layers of carbon atoms. Consequently, within a single crystal, the electrical conductivity of graphite is much greater parallel to the layers than it is at right angles to the layers.

Because graphite combines good electrical conductivity with relative chemical inertness it is often used as a material for the construction of electrodes for industrial electrochemical plants.

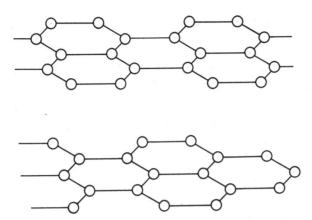

Figure 3 The structure of graphite. The atoms are arranged in layers, each atom within a layer being linked to three others. Between the layers electrons are free to move in a similar way to electrons in a metal.

Energies of reactions

Within an electrically neutral atom, molecule, or crystal the repulsive forces between like charges and the attractive forces between unlike charges balance. If this balance is to be disturbed in any way work has to be done; that is, energy has to be supplied. For example, if we wish to remove one electron from an atom of sodium we must supply 8.2×10^{-19} J of energy to that atom. If we wish to break up a molecule of hydrogen into two hydrogen atoms we must supply 7.2×10^{-19} J of energy to that molecule.

When any chemical reaction takes place, the initial balance existing in the reactant molecules is destroyed, but it is replaced by a new balance existing in the product molecules. Depending, therefore, on the relative energies of the reactants and products, either energy has to be provided to maintain the reaction or it is liberated as a result of the reaction. Very often these energy changes become apparent by the absorption or evolution of heat. Chemical reactions which give out heat are called *exothermic* reactions; those which absorb heat, *endothermic* reactions. The majority of chemical reactions that are observed are exothermic.

The reaction between sodium and fluorine is very exothermic (and very dangerous!). Thus, clearly, the energy stored in the ionic bonds in sodium fluoride is appreciably less than the sum of the energies stored in the metallic bonds in the sodium and in the covalent bonds in the fluorine.

An understanding of the energy changes taking place when reactions occur is extremely important to the chemist: in fact, the study of chemistry is basically the study of the ways in which atoms are rearranged in chemical reactions and of the associated energy changes which take place. Although these changes often become apparent by the absorption or evolution of heat, other forms of energy may be involved. Radiant energy, either as visible light or as radiation in other parts of the electro-magnetic spectrum, may be emitted or absorbed, and the study of this constitutes those branches of chemistry known as *photochemistry* and *chemical spectroscopy*. The energy changes may involve electrical energy and much of electrochemistry is concerned with the chemical changes brought about by electrical energy (electrolysis) and with the electrical energy generated by chemical reactions (galvanic cells). In subsequent chapters we shall study these in some detail.

Electrolytes and Electrolytic Solutions   3

We have seen that crystals of ionic substances (salts) contain no recogniz-able molecules but consist of an assembly of positive and negative ions which are held together by a balance of attractive and repulsive forces between the ions. It is possible to calculate how strongly these ions are bound together (though the calculations are beyond the scope of this book): the values obtained are, for most salts, very high. Now, a char-acteristic of most ionic substances is that their crystals are hard with high melting and boiling points and these properties are just those that would be expected for substances which are held together by strong forces.

Many salts are soluble in water, some considerably so. However, when a salt dissolves in water its component ions become separated from one another. Instead of being packed regularly and compactly in the crystal the ions become free to move about more or less randomly in the solution. How is this possible when the forces holding the ions together in the crystal were so strong?

Part of the answer becomes apparent from a consideration of Coulomb's law (equation 1.2). Water has an exceptionally high dielectric constant and the forces between charged ions in solution are, in con-sequence, approximately one-eighteenth of what they are in the crystal. In confirmation of this it can be noted that salts are not usually soluble in liquids of low dielectric constant. More detailed calculations of the energies involved show, however, that the situation is considerably more complex and that solubility cannot be explained simply in terms of a dielectric constant effect. We need to know more about the nature of the interactions which take place when a salt is dissolved in a solvent, and this requires first some understanding of the structure of that solvent. In this book we shall concern ourselves principally with aqueous solutions and shall therefore now consider in a little detail the structure of liquid water.

The structure of water

It is easy to think of liquids as essentially random aggregates of molecules without any of the regularity of structure shown by crystalline solids. This, however, would give a false picture. All liquids have some regularity of structure: the structure of water is particularly interesting though it is still by no means fully understood.

Water is a molecular substance, the H_2O molecules being held together by strong covalent bonds between the hydrogen atoms and the oxygen atom. These bonds have appreciable ionic characteristics and consequently the molecules of water, like hydrogen fluoride, are polar. Fractional positive charges exist on the two hydrogen atoms with a corresponding doubly fractional negative charge on the oxygen atom. Adjacent water molecules, therefore, interact fairly strongly with one another, the hydrogen atoms on one molecule being attracted by

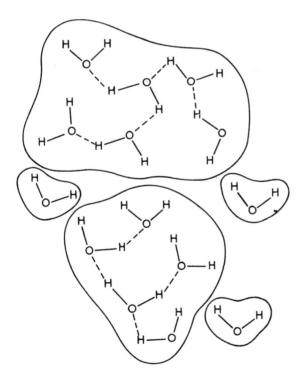

Figure 4 Water molecules in liquid water. Hydrogen bonds (represented by broken lines) cause the molecules to link together into clusters. The clusters are continually breaking down and reforming so that at any instant some molecules are bound in clusters and the remainder are free.

coulombic forces to the oxygen atoms on adjacent molecules. These forces give rise to what are known as *hydrogen bonds* between water molecules. These bonds are responsible for some of the rather unique properties of water; for instance, the fact that it is a liquid at ordinary temperatures whereas the hydrides of the other group VI elements, H_2S, H_2Se, and H_2Te (which are only slightly polar and hence cannot hydrogen-bond), are gases. These bonds cause the molecules in the liquid to group together into molecular clusters as shown in figure 4. These clusters, however, are not fixed unchanging entities but continually break down and reform as individual water molecules move about in the liquid. The clustering is more pronounced at low temperatures; nearer to the boiling point the molecules move about much more rapidly and consequently remain linked in any particular cluster for a much shorter period of time. At a given instant a certain number of molecules (depending on the temperature) will be in clusters and the remainder will be 'free'; that is, in the process of moving from one cluster to another.

Ion hydration

When a salt is dissolved in water the structure of the water is very considerably modified. A positive ion strongly attracts water molecules in such a way that the negatively charged oxygen atoms point towards it (figure 5); conversely, a negative ion attracts water molecules so that the positively charged hydrogen atoms point towards it (figure 6). These effects tend both to disrupt the surrounding clusters and to immobilize the more freely moving water molecules; also a layer of water molecules tends to form on the surface of each dissolved ion. The effects are more pronounced for highly charged ions than for ions of lower charge. The aluminium ion Al^{3+}, for example, attaches a layer of six water molecules to itself very firmly and several other layers rather less firmly. The

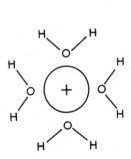

Figure 5 The disposition of water molecules around a positive ion in solution.

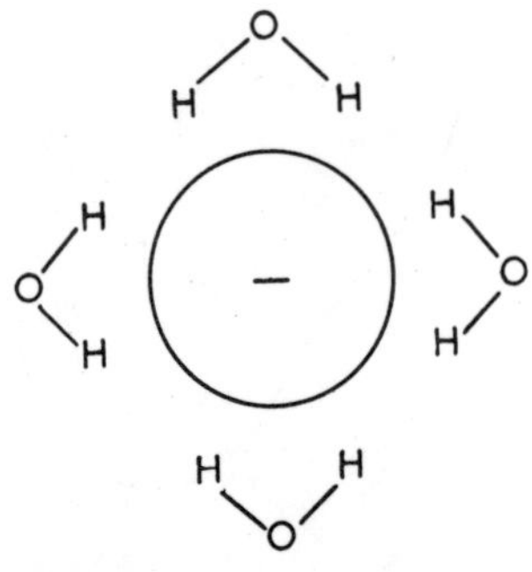

Figure 6 The disposition of water molecules around a negative ion in solution.

potassium ion, having only one positive charge, interacts less strongly and probably only goes so far as to cause some disruption of the adjacent water clusters without actually acquiring a firmly attached layer of molecules. The size of the ion is also important. The lithium ion, Li^+, although having the same charge as potassium, is very much smaller. It can therefore approach water molecules more closely and the consequently stronger coulombic forces give rise to the attachment of probably four molecules. This difference in behaviour between potassium and lithium is exemplified by the fact that lithium salts crystallize with water of crystallization whereas potassium salts form anhydrous crystals.

These complex interactions between ions and water molecules are accompanied by corresponding energy changes. Taken together with the effect of the high dielectric constant they provide sufficient energy to allow the strong forces holding the crystal together to be overcome so that the salt goes into solution.

The sum of all the interactions taking place between ions and water molecules in solution is known as the *hydration of ions*. Ions to which molecules of water have been attached more or less firmly are said to be *hydrated*. Small highly charged ions tend to be strongly hydrated, while larger and less highly charged ions tend to be less hydrated, if at all. However, there is in all cases an appreciable *hydration effect* which has an important bearing on the properties of ions in solution.

When we study the behaviour of ions in solvents other than water we use the more general term *solvation* to describe the interactions taking place.

Electrolysis

If a potential difference is established between two points an electric current can flow, the magnitude of the current depending on that of the potential difference and of the resistance between the points. If the potential difference is between two points in a metallic conductor the current will consist of a flow of electrons, the behaviour of these electrons being explained by theories of metallic bonding. If a potential difference exists between two points in an aqueous solution of a salt a flow of electrons cannot take place because free electrons cannot normally exist in water. However, the ions themselves can move and a movement of positive ions in one direction and of negative ions in the other direction also constitutes an electric current. There is an important difference, however, between conduction of electricity by electrons and by ions. When a current of electrons flows through a metal (or a substance such as graphite which also contains free electrons) the only effect of the current is to heat the metal. When a current of ions flows through a solution not only is heat evolved but a chemical reaction also takes place, the solution being decomposed by the current flow. This phenomenon is known as *electrolysis.* A solution which is capable of being decomposed electrolytically is known as an *electrolytic* solution (or electrolyte solution), the solute being known as an *electrolyte.*

Studies of electrolysis can be carried out in an *electrolytic cell* (figure 7). A potential difference is applied between conductors (metal or graphite) which dip into the solution being studied. The conductors are known as the *electrodes* of the cell. The electrode connected to the positive terminal of the battery (the positive electrode) attracts negative ions present in the solution. Similarly, the negative electrode attracts positive ions. At the surfaces of the electrodes reactions take place which lead to the release or taking up of electrons by the ions concerned. The nature of these reactions depends on a number of factors, particularly the nature and concentration of the solution, the composition of the electrodes, the temperature, the amount of current flowing, and the magnitude of the potential difference between the electrodes. The effect of all these factors must be investigated when an electrolytic process is studied in detail; for example, if it is proposed to use a method based on electrolysis for the preparation of an industrial chemical.

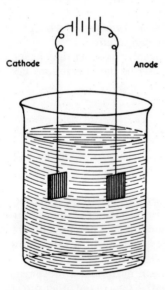

Cathode   Anode

Figure 7 A simple electrolytic cell.

As an example of an electrolytic process let us consider the electrolysis of a solution of zinc chloride using platinum electrodes. First we should note that dissolving zinc chloride in water leads to the hydration processes that we discussed earlier in this chapter. The zinc ions, being small and carrying double positive charges, will be appreciably hydrated; the chloride ions, being much larger and carrying only single charges, much less so. A detailed study of the electrolysis would consider the role of water molecules in the process: in this simplified treatment we shall ignore these and concentrate on what happens to the ions treated simply as Zn^{2+} and Cl^-.

The zinc ions migrate to the negative electrode where the following reaction takes place:

$$Zn^{2+} + 2e^- \rightarrow Zn$$

Each zinc ion, on reaching the electrode, takes up two electrons and is thereby converted to a neutral zinc atom. Continuation of this process leads to the formation of a deposit of zinc on the surface of the platinum electrode.

A process such as this, which involves the taking up, or consumption, of electrons, is known as a *reduction* reaction. In electrochemistry we call an electrode at which a reduction reaction takes place a *cathode*. A positive ion, which will migrate to a cathode, is known as a *cation*.

At the positive electrode, chloride ions reaching the electrode release electrons to produce chlorine atoms:

$$Cl^- \rightarrow Cl + e^-$$

Such a reaction, which involves the release of electrons, is known as an *oxidation* reaction. An electrode at which an oxidation takes place is known as an *anode*. A negative ion, which will migrate to an anode, is known as an *anion*. The number of electrons released in the oxidation reaction at the anode must of course equal the number of electrons consumed in the reduction reaction at the cathode—otherwise the reaction would be creating or destroying electrons. For every atom of zinc deposited at the cathode, therefore, two atoms of chlorine must be formed at the anode:

$$Zn^{2+} + 2e^- \rightarrow Zn$$
$$2Cl^- \rightarrow Cl_2 + 2e^-$$

When these equations are added together the electrons 'cancel out' leaving us with the equation for the overall reaction taking place in the electrolysis cell:

$$ZnCl_2 \rightarrow Zn + Cl_2$$

In effect the battery connected to the cell is an 'electron pump' causing electrons to travel round the circuit and bring about the appropriate anode and cathode reactions. The electrons can be said to act as a catalyst for the total cell reaction.

In the cell just described the positively charged electrode was called the anode and the negatively charged electrode the cathode. In Chapter 7 we shall meet some other kinds of electrochemical cells in which the electrodes known as the anode and cathode are charged in the opposite senses, that is the anode will be negative and the cathode will be positive. Any confusion that might arise over this will be avoided however if it is appreciated that the terms anode and cathode relate not to the signs of the charges on the electrodes but to the processes that take place there. *The anode is the electrode at which an oxidation takes place; the cathode the electrode at which a reduction takes place.*

Let us now consider, in a little more detail, the processes that take place at the anode in our zinc chloride electrolysis cell. As we have seen, chlorine atoms are produced as a result of the oxidation reaction occurring there: subsequently, however, a variety of other reactions is possible. We would, for example, expect chlorine atoms to combine to form molecules:

$$2Cl \rightarrow Cl_2$$

These might appear as bubbles of gas at the surface of the electrode. However, some of this gas could react with the water to give hydrochloric and hypochlorous acids:

$$Cl_2 + H_2O \rightarrow HCl + HOCl$$

The hypochlorous acid might subsequently decompose with the evolution of oxygen:

$$2HOCl \rightarrow 2HCl + O_2$$

A further possibility is that the chlorine atoms might react directly with water molecules to form hydrogen peroxide:

$$Cl + H_2O \rightarrow HCl + OH$$
$$2OH \rightarrow H_2O_2$$

It can be seen, therefore, that the course of a decomposition reaction occurring in an electrolytic cell can be quite complex. In any such reaction a very detailed study is necessary before all the possible reaction stages are known and the influence on them of such factors as concentration, temperature, and voltage has been determined. Only in a few electrolyses are reactions simple and straightforward.

In the sequence of reactions just described the first stage was the formation of a chlorine atom. This is known as a *primary reaction*: subsequent reactions are known as *secondary reactions*.

At the cathode there was only one reaction stage, that of the primary reaction:

$$Zn^{2+} + 2e^- \rightarrow Zn$$

If, however, the reaction had been carried out in a solution of zinc chloride to which hydrochloric acid had been added, an *additional* primary reaction would have been possible leading to the evolution of hydrogen gas:

$$H^+ + e^- \rightarrow H$$
$$2H \rightarrow H_2$$

Example

A solution of copper(II) sulphate was electrolysed in an electrolysis cell containing platinum electrodes. Copper was deposited at electrode A and oxygen at electrode B. Describe the electrode processes taking place.

The deposition of copper requires the uptake of electrons which is a reduction process:

$$Cu^{2+} + 2e^- \rightarrow Cu$$

Electrode A is therefore the cathode of the cell. Sulphate ions migrate to electrode B where they release electrons. This is an oxidation process and B is therefore the anode. However, uncharged sulphate ions cannot exist independently and the reaction taking place also involves water molecules:

$$SO_4{}^{2-} + H_2O \rightarrow H_2SO_4 + O + 2e^-$$
$$2O \rightarrow O_2$$

Faraday's laws of electrolysis

The first systematic study of electrolysis was made by Michael Faraday whose conclusions were contained in two laws, now known as *Faraday's laws*, which were published in 1833 and 1834.

Faraday's *first law* states that in an electrolysis the amount of primary product at each electrode is proportional to the quantity of electricity passed through the cell. Doubling the quantity of electricity passed doubles the amount of primary product. If there is more than one primary reaction the *total* amount of primary products is proportional to the quantity of electricity passed. The first law was established by Faraday using the apparatus shown in figure 8. A current was passed through three electrolysis cells each filled with dilute sulphuric acid, cells 2 and 3 being in parallel with each other and in series with cell 1. The products of the electrolysis of dilute sulphuric acid are hydrogen and oxygen and the volumes of these gases were measured. Faraday found that for both hydrogen and oxygen the amount of gas evolved in cell 1 was equal to the sum of the amounts of gas evolved in cells 2 and 3, thereby establishing the law for this reaction.

Faraday's *second law* states that the masses of different primary products formed by the same quantity of electricity are in the ratio of their chemical equivalents. Faraday established this law by passing a given quantity of electricity through two cells in series, the first containing

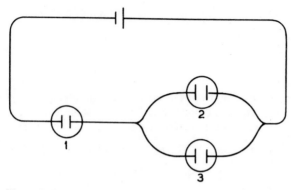

Figure 8 Faraday's apparatus.

dilute sulphuric acid and the second containing molten lead chloride (which contains Pb^{2+} and Cl^- ions and so, like a solution, is subject to electrolytic decomposition). The masses of hydrogen and lead formed were found to be in the ratio of their equivalent weights:

$$\frac{\text{mass of hydrogen}}{\text{mass of lead}} = \frac{\text{equivalent weight of hydrogen}}{\text{equivalent weight of lead}}$$

(The term 'equivalent weight' is used less frequently today. It is equal to A/z where A is the relative atomic mass and z is the charge number* of the substance produced.)

Faraday's laws may be summarized by means of the equation

$$m = \frac{AQ}{zF}$$

where m is the mass of primary product of relative atomic mass A and charge number z produced by the passage of a quantity Q of electricity. F is a constant known as the Faraday constant and is equal to 96 500 C mol^{-1}.

Example

In the electrolysis of a solution of silver nitrate the mass of silver deposited was 0.139 2 g. How much electricity was passed through the solution?

From the equation

$$m = \frac{AQ}{zF}$$

---

*The charge number z is the number of positive or negative charges on the corresponding ion, e.g. $z = 2$ for $Pb^{2+} + 2e \rightarrow Pb$.

we have

m = mass deposited = 0.139 2 g

A = relative atomic mass of silver = 107.9

z = charge number of Ag^+ = 1

F = the Faraday constant = 96 500 C mol^{-1}

and hence

Q = quantity of electricity

$$= \frac{0.139\ 2 \times 1 \times 96\ 500}{107.9}$$

$$= 124.5\ C$$

We now know that electricity is atomic in nature, the *atom* of electricity being called the electron. The presence of a constant quantity of electricity on an electron (which equals 1.602×10^{-19} C) provides a ready and simple explanation of Faraday's laws.

It is not, in fact, easy to verify Faraday's laws experimentally due to various practical difficulties, particularly the formation of secondary products, which tend to make measurements of the amounts of primary products formed inaccurate. However, the existence of electrons and the constancy of their charge has been confirmed in other ways and the correctness of Faraday's laws is now well established.

When more than one primary product is formed, Faraday's laws refer to the total number of equivalents produced. If, in the deposition of a metal from an acid solution, 90 per cent of the current leads to the deposition of metal and 10 per cent to the evolution of hydrogen, the *current efficiency* for metal deposition is 90 per cent and the current efficiency for hydrogen evolution is 10 per cent. The term current efficiency is frequently used in connection with industrial electrochemical processes. In metal plating as high a current efficiency as possible is desirable to avoid wasting electric power in the formation of unwanted side-products. Current efficiencies of 100 per cent are seldom achieved: however, a difference of a few per cent in efficiency may mean the difference between an industrial product being competitive or non-competitive.

Today our more thorough understanding of the atomic nature of matter allows us to appreciate that in an electrolytic reaction one mole of product corresponds to the transfer of zL electrons where L is the Avogadro constant (6.02×10^{23} mol^{-1}). The Faraday constant F is therefore related to the Avogadro constant as follows:

$F = Le$

where e denotes the charge on the electron.

Example

In an acid copper(II) sulphate plating bath, 0.174 9 kg of copper was deposited during the passage of 540 400 C of electricity. What was the current efficiency of the metal deposition process?

From the equation $m = \dfrac{AQ}{zF}$

where

m = mass of copper = 0.174 9 kg = 174.9 g
A = relative atomic mass of copper = 63.54
z = charge number of copper = 2
F = the Faraday constant = 96 500 C mol^{-1}

the quantity of electricity required by Faraday's laws to deposit the copper is

$$Q = \frac{174.9 \times 2 \times 96\,500}{63.54} = 531\,300 \text{ C}$$

However, 540 400 C was actually consumed and the current efficiency was therefore

$$\frac{531\,300}{540\,400} \times 100 = 98.3 \text{ per cent}$$

Inert and active electrodes

The cell for the electrolysis of zinc chloride, discussed earlier in this chapter, contained platinum electrodes. These are *inert* electrodes since platinum does not react with the electrolyte or with the products of electrolysis or undergo any reaction when current flows through the cell. Electrodes can, however, be constructed from materials which will enter into electrolytic reactions; such electrodes are then known as *active* electrodes. If, for example, two copper electrodes are inserted into a solution of copper(II) sulphate and a current is passed through the cell, copper deposits at the cathode:

$$Cu^{2+} + 2e^- \rightarrow Cu$$

but goes into solution at the anode:

$$Cu \rightarrow Cu^{2+} + 2e^-$$

In other words, the anode material itself enters into the reaction. The amount of material which dissolves is, of course, also governed by Faraday's laws.

Problems

1 In the electrolysis of dilute sulphuric acid, in a cell containing platinum electrodes, the products are hydrogen and oxygen. Suggest what reactions take place at the anode and the cathode.

2 A current of 2 A was passed for 2.5 min through a dilute solution of sulphuric acid in an electrolysis cell containing platinum electrodes. Calculate (a) the masses, and (b) the volumes at s.t.p., of the gases evolved, assuming 100 per cent current efficiency.

3 In the manufacture of aluminium, alumina (Al_2O_3) dissolved in molten sodium aluminium fluoride is electrolysed in a cell containing carbon electrodes (see page 93). From such a cell 8.81 kg of aluminium was collected after the passage of 1.08×10^8 C of electricity. Calculate the current efficiency of the aluminium deposition process.

The Classification of Electrolytes   **4**

True and potential electrolytes

Electrolytes are by definition substances which are capable of undergoing electrolysis. A solution of potassium chloride can readily be electrolysed in an electrolytic cell as can also the pure salt when in the molten state. Hydrogen chloride, on the other hand, can be electrolysed when in aqueous solution but not when it is in the pure state. These two substances differ because pure potassium chloride contains ions (it is an ionic substance) whereas pure hydrogen chloride does not (it is an unionized molecular substance). When dissolved in water, however, hydrogen chloride *reacts* to produce ions thereby enabling the solution to conduct electricity:

$$HCl + H_2O \rightarrow H_3O^+ + Cl^-$$

The ion H_3O^+ is known as the *hydronium ion.**

Substances like potassium chloride, which are ionic in the pure state, are known as *true electrolytes*; substances like hydrogen chloride, which

---

*The bare hydrogen ion is simply a proton; this very small particle interacts very strongly with molecules of any solvent, thereby undergoing very considerable solvation. In water it is common to represent the solvated (hydrated) ion as H_3O^+, that is H^+ to which one water molecule has been firmly attached. In fact, it is now considered that four water molecules are involved and the ion is sometimes written as $H_9O_4{}^+$.

form ions only as a result of a chemical reaction with the solvent, are known as *potential electrolytes*. True and potential electrolytes behave in a very similar fashion when in solution but very differently when in the pure state.

Another example of a potential electrolyte is ethanoic (acetic) acid: when dissolved in water this reacts to produce hydronium ions and ethanoate ions:

$$CH_3CO_2H + H_2O \rightarrow H_3O^+ + CH_3CO_2^-$$

However, a comparison of the behaviour of solutions of hydrochloric and ethanoic acids shows considerable differences between the two. The conductivity of a 0.1 M solution of hydrochloric acid is 0.011 2 Ω^{-1} cm^{-1} whereas the conductivity of a solution of ethanoic acid of the same concentration is only 0.000 467 Ω^{-1} cm^{-1}. Further study shows that this difference in behaviour is due to the fact that in solution hydrochloric acid exists completely in the ionic state whereas ethanoic acid is only partly ionized, most of the acid existing in the molecular unionized form. An equilibrium exists between ethanoic acid molecules, water molecules, hydronium ions, and ethanoate ions, which can be expressed by the equilibrium equation

$$CH_3CO_2H + H_2O \rightleftharpoons H_3O^+ + CH_3CO_2^-$$

the split arrow indicating the equilibrium state.

The position of equilibrium is such that in a 0.1 M solution the amount of ionized ethanoic acid is only 1.35 per cent of the total amount of acid present. If the solution is diluted the percentage of acid ionized increases; ionization only becomes complete, however, when the solution is extremely dilute (strictly speaking, when it is infinitely dilute).

Strong and weak electrolytes

Electrolytes which, in solutions of ordinary concentrations, are completely dissociated into ions are known as *strong electrolytes*; those which are incompletely dissociated are known as *weak electrolytes*. However, because solvent molecules enter into the equilibrium reaction, the strength of an electrolyte varies according to the solvent in which it is dissolved. Hydrogen chloride, for example, is a strong electrolyte when dissolved in water but a weak electrolyte when dissolved in the organic solvent, dioxan. Ethanoic acid is a weak electrolyte in water but a strong electrolyte in liquid ammonia.

Water itself is a very weak electrolyte since it undergoes a small amount of *auto-dissociation* by means of the reaction

$$2H_2O \rightleftharpoons H_3O^+ + OH^-$$

At 25 °C the degree of dissociation of pure water is such that the concentrations of hydronium and hydroxide ions are only

$1 \times 10^{-7} \text{mol dm}^{-3}$. At constant temperature the product of these concentrations is a constant:

$$[H_3O^+][OH^-] = K_w \tag{4.1}$$

where the square brackets indicate concentrations and K_w is a constant known as the *ionic product of water*. At 25 °C $K_w = 1 \times 10^{-7} \times 1 \times 10^{-7} = 1 \times 10^{-14} \text{mol}^2 \text{dm}^{-6}$.

Acids and bases

Water is an extremely important liquid and is widely used in chemistry, principally because of its ready availability and because it is such a good solvent. Many substances, when they are dissolved, react with water to give hydronium ions, so increasing the concentration of these above the value of $1 \times 10^{-7} \text{mol dm}^{-3}$. Two examples that we have just met are hydrochloric and ethanoic acids. Substances that can behave in this way are all known as *acids*. Those such as hydrochloric which are completely ionized when in solution and which we have described as strong electrolytes are also known as *strong acids*. Acids such as ethanoic acid, on the other hand, are known as *weak acids*.

Other kinds of substance can *reduce* the concentration of hydronium ions below the value of $1 \times 10^{-7} \text{mol dm}^{-3}$. These substances are known as *bases*. Soluble bases are also known as *alkalis*. An example is sodium hydroxide, a strong electrolyte which is completely ionized into sodium (Na^+) and hydroxide (OH^-) ions. Dissolving this substance in water brings about a reaction between these added hydroxide ions and the hydronium ions already present, resulting in a decrease in the hydronium ion concentration:

$$OH^- + H_3O^+ \rightarrow 2H_2O$$

Sodium hydroxide, being completely ionized in water, is known as a *strong base*.

An example of a *weak base* is ammonia in water. Ammonia is a potential electrolyte which reacts with water to give ammonium and hydroxide ions:

$$NH_3 + H_2O \rightleftharpoons NH_4^+ + OH^-$$

This reaction is only partial, however, most of the ammonia in solution being in the form of neutral molecules. (This is why a solution of ammonia ought not to be labelled 'ammonium hydroxide'.)

So far as solutions in water are concerned, therefore, we might define acids as substances which increase the concentration of hydronium ions and bases as substances which decrease the concentration of hydronium ions. It is desirable however to have definitions which embrace solutions in solvents other than water. We observe that the ability to produce hydronium ions is due to the fact that the substance can donate protons (H^+) to the water molecules. We therefore *define* acids as substances which can behave as *proton donors*. If hydrogen chloride is dissolved in liquid ammonia the following reaction takes place:

$$HCl + NH_3 \rightarrow NH_4^+ + Cl^-$$

In this case the HCl has donated a proton to the ammonia and thus conforms to our general definition of an acid. In this solution the solvated proton is NH_4^+: this corresponds to H_3O^+ in water.

Because bases function by removing protons we define them as *proton acceptors*. Sodium hydroxide is a base because its hydroxide ions accept protons from hydronium ions present in the solvent.

This definition of acids and bases, in terms of proton donation and acceptance, is due to J. N. Brönsted. It is a most important generalization and is of great value in the study of electrolyte solutions. One very important consequence of the Brönsted definition is that many substances are now defined as acids or bases which would not have been thought of as such under older, more restricted definitions. Because the water molecule accepts protons when hydronium ions are formed, the water molecule is itself a base. Conversely when a water molecule donates a proton leaving a hydroxide ion, the water molecule behaves as an acid. Water, therefore, is an *amphoteric* substance, that is, a substance which can behave both as an acid and as a base depending on the nature of the reaction in which it is involved.

Acid/base pairs

If we examine the equation for any reaction involving acids or bases we see that acids and bases always go in pairs:

$$HCl \quad + \quad H_2O \quad \rightarrow \quad H_3O^+ \quad + \quad Cl^-$$

proton donor (acid)   proton acceptor (base)

This, of course, is because proton *donation* is only possible if a proton *acceptor* is present. However, the products also constitute an acid and a base, because it is always possible to reverse the reaction by removing hydrogen chloride from the solution. We can therefore write

$$HCl \quad + \quad H_2O \quad \rightarrow \quad H_3O^+ \quad + \quad Cl^-$$

$acid_1$ $base_2$ $acid_2$ $base_1$

HCl and Cl^- are said to constitute a *conjugate acid/base pair*. Similarly, H_3O^+ and H_2O constitute another conjugate acid/base pair. The general equation for any reaction involving acids and bases will therefore always be

$$acid_1 + base_2 \rightarrow acid_2 + base_1$$

where $acid_1/base_1$ and $acid_2/base_2$ are conjugate pairs.

Let us now consider two further examples.

1 *The reaction between hydrochloric acid and sodium hydroxide*
This reaction is sometimes written

$$HCl + NaOH \rightarrow NaCl + H_2O$$

However, because the acid, the base, and the salt are all completely dissociated in solution, the reaction—taking into account the hydration of the proton—can be written

$$H_3O^+ + Cl^- + Na^+ + OH^- \rightarrow Na^+ + Cl^- + 2H_2O$$

Na^+ and Cl^- appear both on the left- and right-hand sides of the equation, which can therefore be simplified to

$$\underset{\text{acid}_1}{H_3O^+} + \underset{\text{base}_2}{OH^-} \rightarrow \underset{\text{acid}_2}{H_2O} + \underset{\text{base}_1}{H_2O}$$

The right-hand side of this equation emphasizes the amphoteric nature of water, one molecule having been formed by proton donation and one by proton acceptance.

2 *The reaction between ammonia and ethanoic acid*
Ammonia is a weak base and ethanoic acid is a weak acid, so their solutions in water are ionized to a small extent. However, at ordinary concentrations—say, 0.1 M—the two substances are largely in their unionized molecular forms and we are justified in writing the reaction as

$$\underset{\text{acid}_1}{CH_3CO_2H} + \underset{\text{base}_2}{NH_3} \rightarrow \underset{\text{acid}_2}{NH_4^+} + \underset{\text{base}_1}{CH_3CO_2^-}$$

A list of some acids and bases conforming to the Brönsted definition is given in table 5.

Acid	Conjugate base
H_3O^+	H_2O
H_2O	OH^-
HCl	Cl^-
NH_4^+	NH_3
CH_3CO_2H	$CH_3CO_2^-$
H_3PO_4	$H_2PO_4^-$
$H_2PO_4^-$	HPO_4^{2-}
HPO_4^{2-}	PO_4^{3-}

Table 5 Some acids and bases (Brönsted definition).

The strengths of acids and bases

We have so far referred simply to strong and weak acids and bases. It is necessary, however, to have a more precise way of differentiating between acids and bases of different strengths.

If ethanoic acid is dissolved in water the ionization reaction does not go to completion but reaches a state of equilibrium in which the four components (CH_3CO_2H, $CH_3CO_2^-$, H_2O, and H_3O^+) are all present in the solution:

$$CH_3CO_2H + H_2O \rightleftharpoons CH_3CO_2^- + H_3O^+$$

The law of chemical equilibrium tells us that it is possible to write an equation relating the concentrations of all these substances to a constant known as the *equilibrium constant* (K):

$$K = \frac{[CH_3CO_2^-][H_3O^+]}{[CH_3CO_2H][H_2O]}$$

This equation can be simplified somewhat when we observe that the term $[H_2O]$ is essentially constant. In a 0.1 M solution, for example, only about 1.35 per cent of the acid reacts to give ethanoate ions, the remainder existing as simple dissolved molecules. Consequently, the amount of water reacting is an extremely small percentage of the total amount present, and it is a reasonable approximation to make that the concentration of water has remained unchanged by the addition of the acid.* We can therefore combine the $[H_2O]$ term with the equilibrium constant term to give a new expression:

$$K_a = \frac{[CH_3CO_2^-][H_3O^+]}{[CH_3CO_2H]} \qquad (4.2)$$

where K_a is a new constant known as the *acid dissociation constant*. For ethanoic acid at 25 °C the value of K_a is 1.75×10^{-5} mol dm^{-3}.

The acid dissociation constant varies with temperature but is found to be almost independent of concentration.† Values of dissociation constants enable us to compare the strengths of various acids: some of these are given in table 6. Very weak acids have very small dissociation constants; stronger acids have larger values.

Base dissociation constants can be defined in the same way. For ammonia we can write

$$NH_3 + H_2O \rightleftharpoons NH_4^+ + OH^-$$

---

*The concentration of pure water is the same as its density; that is 1.000 g cm^{-3} = 1 000 g dm^{-3}. Alternatively, this concentration can be expressed as 1 000/18 = 55.56 M.

†If K_a were truly a constant it would not, of course, vary at all with concentration. It does, however, vary slightly mainly due to the rather complex way in which charged ions interact with one another. It is only possible to define a quantity which is truly a constant if, instead of concentrations, we use what are known as *activities*: these can be thought of as concentrations corrected to take into account the interactions between ions. The true constant is known as the *thermodynamic dissociation constant*. The difference between this and the constant that we have defined is often small and can be ignored at this stage.

Acid	Conjugate base	$K_a/\text{mol dm}^{-3}$
H_2SO_4	HSO_4^-	1×10^3
HSO_4^-	SO_4^{2-}	1.2×10^{-2}
CH_2ClCO_2H	$CH_2ClCO_2^-$	1.34×10^{-3}
CH_3CO_2H	$CH_3CO_2^-$	1.75×10^{-5}
H_2CO_3	HCO_3^-	4.5×10^{-7}
$HClO$	ClO^-	9.56×10^{-7}
C_6H_5OH	$C_6H_5O^-$	1.2×10^{-10}
HCN	CN^-	4.79×10^{-10}
NH_4^+	NH_3	5.75×10^{-10}
HCO_3^-	CO_3^{2-}	4.7×10^{-11}

Table 6 Dissociation constants of some acids in water at 25 °C.

from which we can define a base dissociation constant K_b as

$$K_b = \frac{[NH_4^+][OH^-]}{[NH_3]} \tag{4.3}$$

It is, however, more usual with bases to quote the dissociation constant of the conjugate acid.

For ammonia the conjugate acid is the ammonium ion and the dissociation constant is defined therefore in terms of the equation

$$NH_4^+ + H_2O \rightleftharpoons NH_3 + H_3O^+$$

that is

$$K_a = \frac{[NH_3][H_3O^+]}{[NH_4^+]} \tag{4.4}$$

Multiplying together equations 4.3 and 4.4 we have

$$K_a K_b = [H_3O^+][OH^-]$$

which equals the ionic product for water, K_w. This relationship is true generally for any conjugate acid/base pair.

Example
The base dissociation constant of ammonia is $K_b = 1.81 \times 10^{-5} \text{ mol dm}^{-3}$. What is its acid dissociation constant?

From the general relationship

$$K_a K_b = K_w$$

we have

$$K_a = \frac{1.00 \times 10^{-14}}{K_b} = \frac{1.00 \times 10^{-14}}{1.81 \times 10^{-5}}$$

$$= 5.52 \times 10^{-10} \text{ mol dm}^{-3}$$

Polyprotic acids and bases

Acids such as hydrochloric and ethanoic which can release one proton for each molecule of acid are known as *monoprotic acids* (sometimes as *monobasic acids*). Acids which are capable of releasing more than one proton are known as *polyprotic acids*. An example of the latter is sulphuric acid which is able to release two protons:

$$H_2SO_4 + H_2O \rightarrow H_3O^+ + HSO_4^-$$
$$HSO_4^- + H_2O \rightleftharpoons H_3O^+ + SO_4^{2-}$$

In its first dissociation sulphuric acid is a strong acid since this dissociation is essentially complete. In its second dissociation, however, sulphuric acid is much weaker, the dissociation constant being 1.2×10^{-2} mol dm^{-3}. Another polyprotic acid, phosphoric acid, can release three protons and so has three dissociation constants:

$$H_3PO_4 + H_2O \rightleftharpoons H_3O^+ + H_2PO_4^-$$
$$H_2PO_4^- + H_2O \rightleftharpoons H_3O^+ + HPO_4^{2-}$$
$$HPO_4^{2-} + H_2O \rightleftharpoons H_3O^+ + PO_4^{3-}$$

Similar behaviour is found with some bases. 1,2-diaminoethane, $H_2N-CH_2-CH_2-NH_2$, for example, has basic groups at each end of the molecule and these can both react with water, so that there are two dissociation constants:

$$H_2N-CH_2-CH_2-NH_2 + H_2O$$
$$\rightleftharpoons H_2N-CH_2-CH_2-NH_3^+ + OH^-$$
$$H_2N-CH_2-CH_2-NH_3^+ + H_2O$$
$$\rightleftharpoons {}^+H_3N-CH_2-CH_2-NH_3^+ + OH^-$$

Problems

1 Potassium chloride is a true electrolyte whereas hydrogen chloride is a potential electrolyte. Discuss the reasons for this difference.

2 Discuss the dissociation of sulphuric acid in aqueous solution in terms of the concepts of strong and weak acids. List all the acid/base pairs and any amphoteric substances present in the solution.

The Conductivity of Electrolytic Solutions **5**

The measurement of conductivity

Electrolytes produce electrically conducting solutions when they are dissolved in appropriate solvents. The conductance of such solutions can be measured by means of a *conductance bridge*, shown in its simplest form in figure 9. This is basically a Wheatstone bridge which is used for measurements of electrical resistance. The solution under examination is

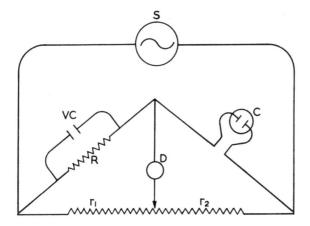

Figure 9 Bridge for the measurement of conductance.

placed in a special cell known as a conductance cell (C) which contains two electrodes, usually made of platinum (figure 10). This cell forms one arm of the bridge, the other arms consisting of a calibrated resistance box (R) and the two halves (r_1 and r_2) of a variable slide wire resistance.

Direct current cannot be used for measurements with this bridge since it would cause electrolysis of the solution and hence a change in its composition. High frequency alternating current from a source S is therefore employed which, by virtue of the fact that it is continually and rapidly reversing its direction, causes no electrolysis. This current is detected by a 'magic eye' detector (D) or some other device which is capable of responding to alternating current. At the balance point, when no current passes through D, the resistance of the solution under

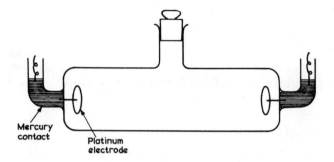

Mercury
contact

Platinum
electrode

Figure 10 One form of conductance cell. The mercury contacts allow connection of the cell to a conductance bridge.

investigation (R_{cell}) is given by the expression

$$R_{cell} = Rr_2/r_1$$

The conductance (G_{cell}) is the reciprocal of this:

$$G_{cell} = 1/R_{cell}$$

The conductance cell, however, behaves as a condenser as well as a resistance and it is necessary to compensate for its capacitance and its resistance before a balance point can be obtained. For this reason a variable capacitance (VC) is placed in parallel with the resistance box and both this and the slide wire are adjusted until balanced.

Modern conductance meters are based on this same Wheatstone bridge network, the various components—a high frequency source, an alternating current detector, calibrated fixed and variable resistances and capacitances—being combined together within an outer container. Adjustment is by means of one or more controls, the conductance then being read directly from a dial.

When the conductance of an electrolyte solution has been measured, the conductivity can be calculated using equations 1.4 and 1.5 (Chapter 1). However, it is generally inconvenient and difficult to measure values of A and l which now represent the area and distance apart of the electrodes in the cell. Consequently, it is usual first to *calibrate* the cell by filling it with a solution of known conductivity (usually a potassium chloride solution, see table 3 in Chapter 1), and then to measure the conductance of this. Since A and l are constants

$$\kappa = KG$$

where $K = l/A$ and is known as the *cell constant*. This cell constant, calculated from the measurement with the potassium chloride solution, can then be used to obtain conductivities of other solutions from their measured conductances.

Example

In the measurement of the conductivity of a solution of 0.1 M hydrochloric acid the conductance cell was first calibrated with a solution of 0.1 M potassium chloride. The conductance of the potassium chloride solution was found to be $9.047 \times 10^{-3} \, \Omega^{-1}$ and that of the hydrochloric acid $2.718 \times 10^{-2} \, \Omega^{-1}$. What was the conductivity of the hydrochloric acid?

The cell constant K is first obtained from the relationship

$$\kappa = KG$$

κ for 0.1 M potassium chloride is $1.167 \times 10^{-2} \, \Omega^{-1} \, cm^{-1}$ and hence

$$K = \frac{1.167 \times 10^{-2}}{9.047 \times 10^{-3}} = 1.290 \, cm^{-1}$$

This figure is then used with the data for hydrochloric acid to give

$$\kappa = 1.290 \times 2.718 \times 10^{-2} = 3.506 \times 10^{-2} \, \Omega^{-1} \, cm^{-1}$$

Molar conductivity

The conductivity of an electrolyte solution is not of very great interest to the chemist. Of much greater value is the *molar conductivity*, Λ, which is the conductivity divided by the molar concentration c:

$$\Lambda = \kappa/c$$

It is therefore the conductivity of one mole of the electrolyte.

Example

Using the result from the example above calculate the molar conductivity of 0.1 M hydrochloric acid.

In the example quoted the conductivity of the acid was found to be $3.506 \times 10^{-2} \, \Omega^{-1} \, cm^{-1}$. We can now use the equation $\Lambda = \kappa/c$ to obtain the molar conductivity. However, we must be very careful over our choice of units. Conductivities have been expressed in $\Omega^{-1} \, cm^{-1}$ but the concentration is quoted in mol dm^{-3} (0.1 M). To avoid mixing up these units we must convert our concentration into mol cm^{-3} (moles per cubic centimetre).* This is $0.1/1\,000 = 1 \times 10^{-4} \, mol \, cm^{-3}$ and substituting into the equation gives

$$\Lambda = \frac{3.506 \times 10^{-2}}{1 \times 10^{-4}} = 350.6 \, \Omega^{-1} \, mol^{-1} \, cm^2$$

*Conductivities are now sometimes expressed in $\Omega^{-1} \, m^{-1}$ and molar conductivities in $\Omega^{-1} \, mol^{-1} \, m^2$. These are compatible with concentrations expressed in mol m^{-3} (moles per cubic metre).

Conductivities of strong electrolytes

It might be expected that the molar conductivity would be independent of concentration for strong electrolytes. Since such substances are completely dissociated in solution the number of current carriers (anions and cations) does not change as the solution is made more dilute by adding solvent. However, when measurements are actually carried out, it is found that the molar conductivity does change appreciably as shown in figure 11. When conductance studies were made in the latter part of the last century the Swedish chemist Arrhenius explained these observations by proposing that electrolytes in solution were *partially* dissociated into ions, the degree of dissociation varying with the concentration. This theory represented a considerable advance in scientific understanding for until then there had been no clear idea of the nature of such solutions. However, we now know that this theory of *partial dissociation* is incorrect for electrolytes such as potassium chloride which we consider to be completely dissociated in aqueous solution. The explanation of their behaviour lies in the fact that, although the electrolyte is completely dissociated, the ions are not completely independent.

In a very dilute solution of potassium chloride, say, the ions are separated from one another by distances which are very large compared with the sizes of the ions. They are therefore able to move through the

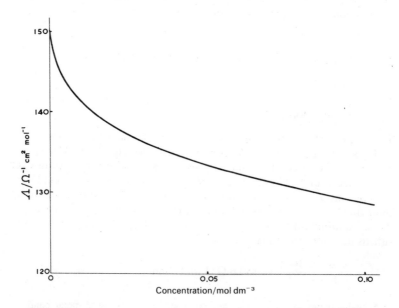

Figure 11 The variation with concentration of the molar conductivity of potassium chloride solution.

solution under the influence of an applied electric field more or less independently of one another. In more concentrated solutions, however, the attractive forces between ions of opposite charge become more significant, positive ions tending to attract around them a number of negative ions and negative ions tending to attract a number of positive ions. The charges on these surrounding ions tend to shield ions from the electric field and these thereby move more slowly towards the electrode. The more concentrated the solution the greater is this effect: the molar conductivity therefore decreases as the concentration increases.

A second factor also reduces the rate of movement of ions towards the electrodes and hence reduces the molar conductivity. Cations moving in one direction are travelling against a counter movement of anions in the opposite direction (similarly anions are moving against a counter movement of cations). These ions are carrying some associated water molecules with them and hence the ions are 'swimming against the current'. This effect is more pronounced as the concentration increases.

If molar conductivity is plotted against the square root of concentration the curves shown in figure 12 are obtained. Extrapolation of these to the y-axis gives the *molar conductivity at zero concentration* Λ_0.*

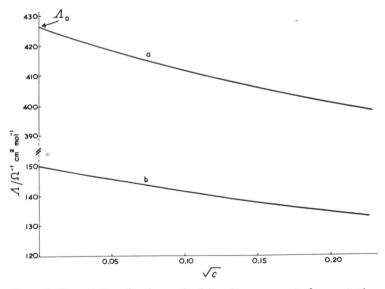

Figure 12 The variation of molar conductivity with square root of concentration for (a) hydrochloric acid and (b) potassium chloride. (Note the break in the scale.)

*This is not the same as the conductivity of pure water. It is the conductivity of one mole of electrolyte dissolved in an infinite amount of water. It cannot, of course, be measured directly but can only be obtained by extrapolation.

The conductivities of ions

The molar conductivities of electrolytes are of particular interest in that they can be broken down into separate conductivities for the individual ions.* The conductivity of potassium chloride, for example, can be written

$$\Lambda(KCl) = \Lambda(K^+) + \Lambda(Cl^-)$$

where $\Lambda(K^+)$ and $\Lambda(Cl^-)$ are the molar conductivities of the potassium and chloride ions.

The conductivities at zero concentration for the individual ions are constants, being independent of the other ion with which the ion in question is associated. For example, $\Lambda_0(K^+)$ is the same for the potassium ion in both potassium chloride solution and potassium sulphate solution. Observations such as these have done much to establish our present understanding of the nature of electrolyte solutions. Some Λ_0 values for ions are given in table 7.

Cations	Λ_0/Ω^{-1} cm^2 mol^{-1}	Anions	Λ_0/Ω^{-1} cm^2 mol^{-1}
H_3O^+	349.8	OH^-	198.3
Li^+	38.7	F^-	55.4
Na^+	50.9	Cl^-	76.4
K^+	74.5	NO_3^-	71.5
Mg^{2+}	106.1	SO_4^{2-}	160.0
Ca^{2+}	119.0		
Cu^{2+}	113.2		
La^{3+}	209.2		

Table 7 Molar conductivities of some ions (aqueous solutions at 25 °C).

Example

The molar conductivity at zero concentration (Λ_0) of sodium ethanoate solution is found to be 91.0 Ω^{-1} mol^{-1} cm^2. What is Λ_0 for the ethanoate ion?

In table 7, Λ_0 for the sodium ion is quoted as 50.9 Ω^{-1} mol^{-1} cm^2. From the equation

$$\Lambda_0(CH_3CO_2Na) = \Lambda_0(Na^+) + \Lambda_0(CH_3CO_2^-)$$

we have

$$\Lambda_0(CH_3CO_2^-) = 91.0 - 50.9$$
$$= 40.1 \ \Omega^{-1} \ mol^{-1} \ cm^2$$

*This is done by measuring the relative speeds of the ions and involves the study of the relative rates of electrolysis reactions occurring at anode and cathode.

Hydronium and hydroxide ion conductivities

An examination of the ionic conductivities given in table 7 shows that the conductivities of the hydronium and hydroxide ions are exceptionally high compared with the values given for other singly charged ions. The explanation lies in the detailed structure of these ions and in the inter- actions that they undergo with neighbouring water molecules. In aqueous solution the hydronium ion is attached by hydrogen bonds to surrounding water molecules as shown diagrammatically in figure 13(i). The positive charge which is located on the hydronium ion can be trans- ferred to an adjacent water molecule (which is thereby transformed into a hydronium ion) by the conversion of a covalent bond into a hydrogen bond and a hydrogen bond into a covalent bond—figure 13(ii). This change simply involves electron movement and, because electrons are very light, takes place very rapidly.* A continuance of this process along a linked chain of water molecules occurs when hydronium ions conduct an electric current. It is easy to see, therefore, why the molar conductivity of the hydronium ion is much greater than that of the sodium ion, say, which is so much more massive, and therefore slower, than the electron.

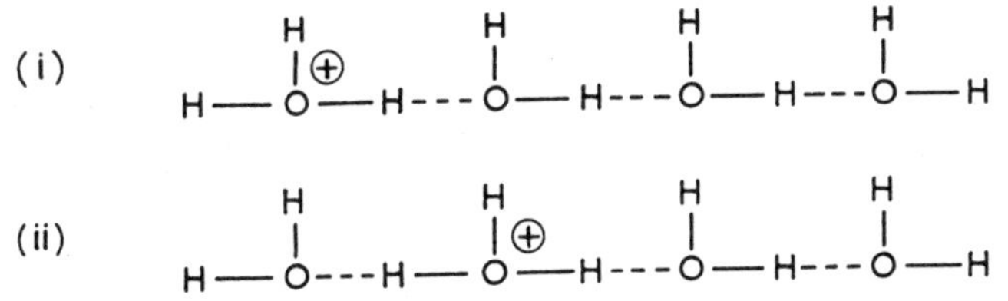

Figure 13 Movement of positive charge in a solution of hydronium ions. This can take place by the simple interconversion of a covalent bond (solid line) and a hydrogen bond (broken line).

A similar effect takes place with the hydroxide ion (figure 14) and accounts for the high conductivity of this ion.

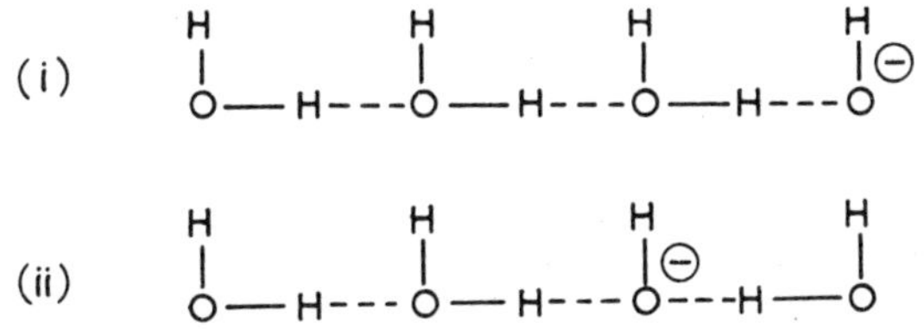

Figure 14 Movement of negative charge in a solution of hydroxide ions.

*There is also a very small associated movement of hydrogen atoms because hydrogen bonds are slightly longer than covalent bonds.

Conductivities of weak electrolytes

When we come to study the conductance behaviour of weak electrolytes we find a different situation from that for strong electrolytes. The conductances of weak electrolytes are of course much lower than those of strong electrolytes because they contain far fewer ions. Also if molar conductivity is plotted against the square root of concentration we find the type of curve shown in figure 15. The explanation of this lies in the

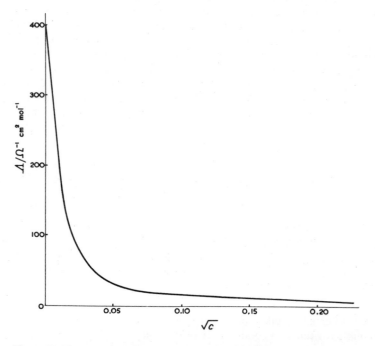

Figure 15 The variation of molar conductivity with square root of concentration for ethanoic acid. Contrast the shape of this curve with those shown in figure 12.

fact that weak electrolytes are only incompletely dissociated and that as the solution becomes more dilute the number of ions in one mole of electrolyte increases, thereby increasing the actual number of charge carriers. Consequently, the conductivity increases much more rapidly than it does for a strong electrolyte. Arrhenius's theory is therefore substantially correct so far as weak electrolytes are concerned. The same kinds of interactions between ions that were described for strong electrolytes are also present but they are small in comparison with the effect of increasing dissociation.

Example

Calculate Λ_0 for ethanoic acid.

As we see in figure 15 the molar conductivity of a solution of a weak acid increases rapidly as the concentration is decreased. Λ_0, therefore, cannot be obtained by extrapolation as in the case of a strong acid (figure 12). However, we can use the relationship

$$\Lambda_0(CH_3CO_2H) = \Lambda_0(H_3O^+) + \Lambda_0(CH_3CO_2^-)$$

$\Lambda_0(H_3O^+)$ is quoted in table 7 as $349.8 \; \Omega^{-1} \, mol^{-1} \, cm^2$. $\Lambda_0(CH_3CO_2^-)$ was calculated in the example on page 34 as $40.1 \; \Omega^{-1} \, mol^{-1} \, cm^2$, and hence

$$\Lambda_0(CH_3CO_2H) = 349.8 + 40.1 = 389.9 \; \Omega^{-1} \, mol^{-1} \, cm^2$$

Problems

1 The conductance of a 1 M solution of potassium chloride, measured in a particular conductance cell, was found to be $8.87 \times 10^{-2} \, \Omega^{-1}$. Calculate the cell constant of the cell.

2 A 0.01 M solution of silver nitrate was diluted three times and the conductance of each solution measured in the cell used in problem 1. Calculate the conductivity of each solution.

Concentration of AgNO$_3$	Conductance/Ω^{-1}
0.000 5 M	5.711×10^{-5}
0.001 M	1.113×10^{-4}
0.005 M	5.543×10^{-4}
0.01 M	1.078×10^{-3}

3 Calculate the molar conductivity of each of the silver nitrate solutions in problem 2. Estimate graphically the molar conductivity at zero concentration.

4 The following conductivities were measured for solutions of aqueous ammonia.

Concentration of ammonia	Conductivity/$\Omega^{-1} \, cm^{-1}$
0.000 1 M	9.30×10^{-6}
0.000 5 M	2.35×10^{-6}
0.001 M	3.40×10^{-5}
0.005 M	8.00×10^{-5}
0.01 M	1.13×10^{-4}
0.05 M	4.00×10^{-4}

Calculate the molar conductivity of each solution, and plot the values in an appropriate graphical form. What conclusions can be drawn about the nature of aqueous ammonia as an electrolyte?

Some Properties of Acids and Bases 6

As we saw in Chapter 4, acids and bases are substances which, in aqueous solution, liberate or remove hydronium ions. There are many occasions when we wish to measure and record the concentrations of these ions and the question first arises of what are the most convenient units to use. We might of course consider the usual concentration units of moles per cubic decimetre. However, the concentration of hydronium ions in a 1 M solution of hydrochloric acid is 10^{14} times greater than in a 1 M solution of sodium hydroxide and a concentration scale covering such a wide range would be somewhat inconvenient to use.

In 1909 Sørensen proposed the adoption of a scale known as the pH scale (pH = *p*ower of *H*ydrogen); his definition of pH being

$$pH = -\lg[H_3O^+] \tag{6.1}$$

Unfortunately it is not, in general, possible to measure accurately the hydronium ion concentrations of solutions. The reasons are complex and beyond the scope of this book: they mean however that the Sørensen equation cannot be used as the basis of a *precise* definition of pH. Fortunately the situation is not hopeless for, as we shall see in Chapter 8, it is possible to carry out measurements with certain galvanic cells which give something closely related to hydronium ion concentrations. We can, therefore, use the Sørensen equation as a working expression when we are not concerned about being very precise, and we shall do this in this book. A truly satisfactory definition of pH will however await a more detailed understanding by the student of the thermodynamics of electrolyte solutions.

The pH range

Using the Sørensen equation, and assuming that strong acids and strong bases are completely dissociated into ions in aqueous solutions, we find that in going from a 1 M solution of a strong acid to a 1 M solution of a strong base we cover a pH range from 0 to 14, the neutral point (pure water) being at pH 7 (25 °C). If we were to go into more concentrated solutions we should extend this to negative values and to values greater than 14. However, we do not usually make pH measurements in such concentrated solutions, and in any case the Sørensen equation then becomes much less satisfactory.

In non-aqueous solutions it is possible to define analogous pH scales.

In liquid ammonia we have

$$pH = -lg[NH_4{}^+]$$

since $NH_4{}^+$ is the form of the solvated proton in such solutions. The pH range is determined by the value of the constant for the dissociation

$$2NH_3 \rightleftharpoons NH_4{}^+ + NH_2{}^-$$

which takes place to a small extent in liquid ammonia. This is equal to

$$K_{amm} = [NH_4{}^+][NH_2{}^-] = 1 \times 10^{-22}\,mol^2\,dm^{-6}\,(-40\,°C)$$

and the normal pH range in liquid ammonia is therefore from 0 to 22 with the neutral point at pH 11.

Other solvents have shorter or longer pH ranges depending on the value of the dissociation constant of the solvent.

Indicators

There are many occasions when measurements of the pH of solutions are necessary: for example, the research chemist studying the properties of a new compound; the industrial chemist wishing to find out if some waste liquid can safely be run into the public sewer; the food chemist determining the edibility and palatability of a new product. The most precise way of measuring pH is by means of a galvanic cell (Chapter 8) but there are occasions when a less precise but simpler method will be preferred. In these cases we can use substances known as *indicators*.

Most indicators are weak acids and they ionize in solution just as any weak acid does. If we write HIn as a general formula for an indicator then, in aqueous solution, we have

$$HIn + H_2O \rightleftharpoons H_3O^+ + In^-$$

The important property of an indicator is that the colours of the molecule HIn and the ion In^- are different. In the case of the indicator methyl orange, for example, the molecule is coloured red and the ion yellow. In a strongly acidic solution the high concentration of hydronium ions already present causes the equilibrium to be shifted over to the left. In this situation the colour of the indicator is that of the unionized HIn form. In a strongly alkaline solution, the high concentration of hydroxide ions, by reacting with the hydronium ions from the indicator, causes the equilibrium to shift to the right. In this case the colour of the indicator is that of the ionized In^- form.

Another important characteristic of an indicator is that the intensity of colour of one or both of its two forms is very great. Consequently, the addition of a few drops of an indicator solution to a liquid under test is sufficient to show whether it is acidic or alkaline.

For an indicator which is a weak acid, it is possible to write an acid dissociation constant just as we did for an acid such as ethanoic acid. In this case we call the dissociation constant the *indicator constant*: it is defined by the expression

$$K_{\text{ind}} = \frac{[H_3O^+][In^-]}{[HIn]} \tag{6.2}$$

The colours and indicator constants of some important indicators are given in table 8. Indicator constants are often quoted in the form pK_{ind} where $pK_{\text{ind}} = -\lg K_{\text{ind}}$. It is common in electrochemistry to use the Sørensen 'p' notation for the negative of the logarithm of a quantity.

Indicator	Colour		pK_{ind}
	Low pH	High pH	$(= -\lg K_{\text{ind}})$
a Thymol blue	red	yellow	1.51
b Methyl orange	red	yellow	3.7
c Bromocresol green	yellow	blue	4.67
d Methyl red	red	yellow	5.1
e Chlorophenol red	yellow	red	6.0
f Bromothymol blue	yellow	blue	7.0
g Phenol red	yellow	red	7.9
h Thymol blue	yellow	blue	8.9
i Phenolphthalein	colourless	red	9.4
j Alizarin yellow	yellow	lilac	11

Table 8 Indicator constants and colours of some indicators.

Equation 6.2 can be rearranged to give

$$\frac{[In^-]}{[HIn]} = \frac{K_{\text{ind}}}{[H_3O^+]}$$

This gives the ratio of the concentrations of the two coloured forms of the indicator in a solution of any given pH. A large value of this ratio means that most of the indicator is in the ionized form and consequently displays the colour of In^-. A small ratio means that most of the indicator is in the unionized form and displays the colour of HIn. If the ratio is unity the solution contains equal concentrations of the two forms and the colour is intermediate between these.

If we plot a graph of fraction of indicator ionized as a function of pH we obtain the shape shown in figure 16 which has been calculated for an indicator having $pK_{\text{ind}} = 4.67$. The shaded portions indicate the pH regions where the fraction of indicator ionized is such that the solution clearly displays either one colour or the other. There is, in between, a region over which the colour will be seen to change: the extent of this region depends on the actual colours of the particular indicator and also on the type of illumination and the sensitivity of the eye of the observer. It can usually be taken to extend over the range from about pH = $pK_{\text{ind}} - 1$ to about pH = $pK_{\text{ind}} + 1$. Within this range it is possible to estimate the pH of a solution by adding an indicator to it and comparing

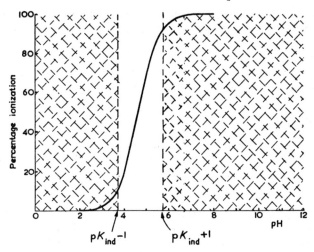

Figure 16 The percentage ionization of an indicator of $pK_{ind} = 4.67$ as a function of pH. The shaded portions show the regions where the indicator displays the colour of HIn (left-hand side) or that of In$^-$ (right-hand side).

the colour produced with the colours of a set of samples containing the same concentration of the indicator in solutions of known pH.* This estimation can be done by eye or more accurately by a spectrophotometer.

In figure 17 are shown plots of fraction of indicator ionized against pH

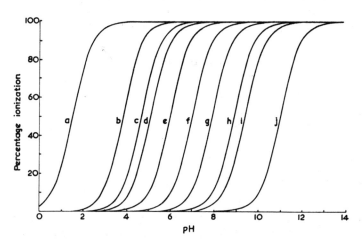

Figure 17 The percentage ionization of the indicators listed in table 8 as a function of pH.

*Buffer solutions. See page 45.

for the indicators listed in table 8. It will be seen that these allow observations to be made over any desired range by choosing the appropriate indicator.

By mixing together different indicators, solutions can be obtained which will display many colour changes over an extended pH range. Such mixtures are known as *universal indicators*.

Acid/base titrations

Indicators are very commonly used in *acid/base titrations*: these are reactions between solutions of acids and bases which enable the concentration of one or the other substance to be determined.

Titration of a strong acid with a strong base

To understand the part that indicators play let us consider how the pH of a solution of an acid changes as a solution of a base is gradually added to it. We will take as an example a solution of 50 cm³ of 0.1 M HCl to which are added amounts of a solution of 0.1 M NaOH.

The pH of the hydrochloric acid is initially equal to one (pH $= -\lg 0.1$). If 25 cm³ of the hydroxide is added, half the acid is neutralized and converted to sodium chloride. At the same time the volume of the solution increases to 75 cm³. The pH then becomes $-\lg[0.1 \times (50 - 25)/75]$ or pH $= 1.48$. On adding another 20 cm³ of hydroxide the pH becomes $-\lg[0.1 \times (50 - 45)/95]$ or pH $= 2.28$. As further amounts of sodium hydroxide are added the pH changes as shown in table 9. This calculation assumes, however, that all the hydronium ion comes from the hydrochloric acid: this is basically true at the start of the titration because the water is only very slightly dissociated into hydronium and hydroxide ions.

Volume of base added/cm³	pH (calculated from pH $= -\lg[H_3O^+]$)
0	1.00
25	1.48
45	2.28
48	2.69
49	3.00
49.5	3.30
49.9	4.00

Table 9 Titration of 0.1 M HCl (50 cm³) with 0.1 M NaOH.

However, as the titration proceeds the contribution from the acid becomes less significant and at the point when the stoichiometric amounts of acid and base have been mixed (the *stoichiometric* or *end-point*), all the hydronium ion in solution comes from the water, the hydrochloric acid having been neutralized. At this point, therefore, the pH is 7, the pH of pure water. On adding more sodium hydroxide the pH increases due to the added hydroxide ion; the pH values calculated in this way are given in table 10 and are plotted in figure 18. Examination of this plot shows that the pH changes only slowly at the start and finish of the titration but very rapidly in the immediate region of the stoichiometric point.

Volume of base added/cm³	pH (calculated from pH $= -\lg [H_3O^+]$)
50.1	10.00
50.5	10.70
51	11.00
52	11.29
55	11.68
75	12.30
100	12.52

Table 10 Titration of 0.1 M HCl (50 cm³) with 0.1 M NaOH (beyond the stoichiometric point).

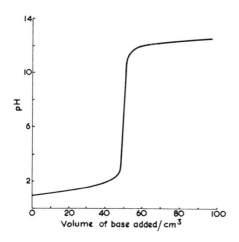

Figure 18 The titration curve of 50 cm³ of 0.1 M HCl with 0.1 M NaOH.

Now, it was shown earlier in this chapter that indicators change colour over a pH range extending from about $pK_{ind} - 1$ to $pK_{ind} + 1$. In figure 19 this range for indicators having pK values of 1.51 and 5.1 has been superimposed on the neutralization curve of figure 18. It is clear that if an indicator of $pK = 5.1$ were added to the acid being titrated it would undergo a sudden colour change at the stoichiometric point because of the rapid pH change which occurs there. On the other hand, if the indicator of $pK = 1.51$ had been used there would have been only a gradual colour change which would have given no indication of the stoichiometric point.

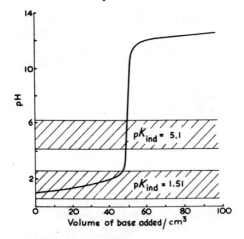

Figure 19 Choice of indicator for the titration curve of figure 18. The shaded portions indicate the regions in which there is a colour change for indicators having pK_{ind} values of 1.51 and 5.1.

Example

50 cm^3 of a 0.01 M solution of hydrochloric acid was titrated with 0.01 M sodium hydroxide. The pH of the mixture was measured with a pH meter during the course of the titration and the following figures obtained:

Volume of base added/cm³	pH	Volume of base added/cm³	pH
0	2.0	51	10.0
10	2.2	52	10.3
20	2.4	53	10.5
30	2.6	54	10.6
40	3.0	55	10.7
45	3.3	60	11.0
46	3.4	70	11.2
47	3.5	80	11.4
48	3.7	90	11.5
49	4.0	100	11.5
50	7.0		

What indicator would be suitable for this titration?

If pH is plotted against volume of base added it will be found that the near vertical portion of the curve extends from about pH 4 to pH 10.

From table 8 it will be seen that methyl red changes colour over the pH range of approximately 4.1 to 6.1 and this should therefore be a suitable indicator to use. Examination of the table will suggest some others.

Titration of a weak acid with a strong base
The shapes of titration curves depend on the concentrations of acid and base used and on whether the acids and bases are strong or weak electrolytes (that is on the value of the acid dissociation constant). For the case of a 0.1 M solution of ethanoic acid titrated with 0.1 M sodium hydroxide the shape of the curve is as shown in figure 20. The most significant feature of this curve is that the vertical portion, which occurs at the stoichiometric point, is no longer centred on pH = 7 but is shifted higher up on the pH scale. This has the result that an indicator which would be suitable for the titration of hydrochloric acid would be unsuitable for ethanoic acid and one of higher pK_{ind} must be used.

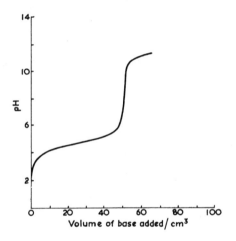

Figure 20 The titration curve of 50 cm³ of 0.1 M ethanoic acid with 0.1 M NaOH.

Choice of indicator

Before an acid can be titrated it is essential that the correct indicator is chosen: this can only be done if the shape of the titration curve for the particular system is known. For hydrochloric acid and other strong acids, methyl orange is usually satisfactory if the acid concentration is about 0.1 M; at lower concentrations methyl red should be used. For ethanoic acid, at about 0.1 M concentration, phenolphthalein is satisfactory. Phenolphthalein can also be used for other weak acids with dissociation constants which are not too different from that of ethanoic acid.

The chemist has available to him a great many indicators covering the normal pH range and it is not difficult to choose one that is appropriate to a desired titration.

Buffers

There are occasions when it is necessary to carry out reactions in a solution of constant pH. In nickel plating for example (page 92) the pH of the plating bath must not go too high or the deposited metal will be spoiled by the simultaneous precipitation of nickel hydroxide. On the other hand, the pH must not go too low or appreciable amounts of electric current will be wasted in simply bringing about the evolution of hydrogen gas. However, many chemical reactions, as they proceed, consume or liberate hydrogen ions and this can itself bring about a pH change. The electrolysis of a metal sulphate solution, for example, might convert the salt into sulphuric acid with a consequent decrease in the pH of the solution.

To maintain the pH of a solution at a constant, or nearly constant, value a *buffer* must be used. Buffers are substances, or mixtures of substances, which by their presence in a solution permit hydronium ions to be added or removed without causing any significant change of pH.

To understand how buffers function let us re-examine the titration curves which were discussed earlier in this chapter. In figure 18 it can be seen that at the start and finish of the titration there is a very slow change of pH even though appreciable amounts of base are being added. In the region of the stoichiometric point however a very small addition of base brings about a very large pH change. For example, the first 49 cm^3 of added base changes the pH only from 1.00 to 3.00 whereas adding only a further 0.2 cm^3 when 49.9 cm^3 has been added changes the pH from 4.00 to 10.00. If one wished therefore to maintain the pH of a solution fairly constant somewhere between pH 1 and 3 this could be done by adding a sufficient amount of a strong acid.

If we consider now the titration curve for ethanoic acid (figure 20) we see that there are significant pH changes at the start of the titration and at the stoichiometric point but that there is a region where the pH remains fairly constant at around pH 4.5. A buffer to maintain pH in this region could therefore be made from ethanoic acid to which has been added an appropriate amount of sodium hydroxide.

The effectiveness of a particular buffer solution can be measured by what is known as its buffer capacity β. This is given by the expression

$$\beta = \frac{\text{amount of base added}}{\text{corresponding pH change}}$$

If we read off from figure 20 the pH changes corresponding to the addition of successive 1 cm^3 amounts of sodium hydroxide, we can then calculate β for 0.1 M ethanoic acid as a function of pH. The results are shown in figure 21. Clearly the buffer capacity is extremely low in the pH

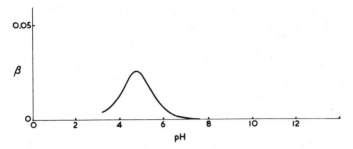

Figure 21 The buffer capacity curve for 0.1 M ethanoic acid.

regions below about 3 and above about 6: these correspond to the beginning of the titration curve when there is a significant change of pH, and to the region of the stoichiometric point when there is another significant change. In the region 4 to 5.5, however, the buffer capacity is large and has a maximum at pH 4.75. This is the point at which the titration is half complete, that is, when the acid is half neutralized. A buffer solution to stabilize pH at 4.75 could therefore be made up by adding sufficient sodium hydroxide to a solution of ethanoic acid to half neutralize it, or, rather more simply, by mixing together equal amounts of ethanoic acid and sodium ethanoate.

Figure 22 shows the buffer capacity curves for a number of substances.

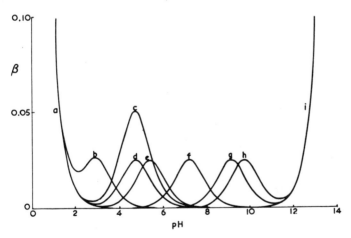

Figure 22 The buffer capacity curves for various substances. The concentrations are all 0.1 M except curve c: (a) hydrochloric acid; (b) potassium hydrogen phthalate; (c) ethanoic acid (0.2 M); (d) ethanoic acid (0.1 M); (e) succinic acid; (f) potassium hydrogen phosphate; (g) boric acid; (h) glycine; (i) sodium hydroxide.

They show that it is possible to make up buffer solutions which will stabilize pH at various acidic and alkaline values. Many more substances can be used as buffers, and solutions can be made up which will operate at any desired pH. Tables of these are given in many of the standard chemical reference books. For some purposes *buffer tablets* can be used. These are made up from mixtures of solid chemicals: when dissolved according to the manufacturer's instructions they produce buffers of a quoted pH value.

Buffers are extremely important in most branches of chemistry and particularly in analytical chemistry, biochemistry, and industrial chemistry. Many biological processes are critically dependent on buffers: for instance the pH of blood is buffered naturally at 7.2 and a small change from this value can lead to serious illness or death.

In using buffers the possibility of undesirable reactions with the buffer must always be anticipated. There would, for example, be little point in attempting to use a phosphate buffer with a solution containing calcium ion if the buffer were thereby immediately precipitated out as calcium phosphate. It should also be remembered that no buffer has an infinite capacity and will always undergo some pH change when it is used. The particular buffer and the concentration in which it is used must therefore be such that any change is within acceptable limits.

Problems

1 The curve for the titration of 50 cm³ of a 0.1 M acid with 0.1 M sodium hydroxide is shown in figure 23. Discuss the shape of this curve

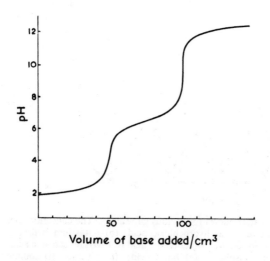

Figure 23

in terms of the dissociation of the acid. What indicators could be used for the titration and what information would they provide?

2 Define pH and list the neutral points and normal pH ranges for the following solvents.

Solvent	Ionization	Ionic product/$mol^2\ dm^{-6}$
Ammonia	$2NH_3 \rightleftharpoons NH_4^+ + NH_2^-$	1×10^{-22}
Methanol	$2CH_3OH \rightleftharpoons CH_3OH_2^+ + CH_3O^-$	1×10^{-17}
Ethanoic acid	$2CH_3CO_2H \rightleftharpoons CH_3CO_2H_2^+$	
	$\qquad\qquad + CH_3CO_2^-$	1×10^{-13}
Sulphuric acid	$2H_2SO_4 \rightleftharpoons H_3O^+ + HS_2O_7^-$	7×10^{-5}

Galvanic Cells and the Origin of Electromotive Force　7

Any chemical reaction involves (*a*) a rearrangement of atoms, and (*b*) an associated movement of electrons. In the reaction between a molecule of hydrogen and a molecule of iodine, for example, the atoms rearrange themselves by changing partners; at the same time the electrons present in the covalent bonds of the reacting molecules move to new positions in the covalent bonds of the hydrogen iodide molecules (figure 24).*

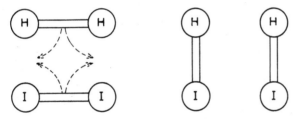

Figure 24 The reaction between a hydrogen molecule and an iodine molecule showing electron movements.

However, a movement of electrons constitutes an electric current; we might, therefore, imagine minute electric currents flowing between molecules during the course of a chemical reaction. These electric currents are, of course, of no use to us as such: they only give rise to energy changes in the reaction system which become apparent by the evolution, or occasionally the absorption, of heat.

*The detailed mechanism of this reaction is rather complex.

However, if we could devise a reaction system in such a way that all the electron movements took place through an external electrical conductor then we should be able to obtain a useful electric current and to gain some of the energy released in the reaction not as heat but as electrical energy. Such a system is known as a *galvanic cell*, after Luigi Galvani (1737–1798) who first demonstrated the production of electricity in this way.

The Daniell cell

As an example, let us consider the reaction between zinc and copper(II) sulphate. If we add zinc powder to a solution of copper(II) sulphate in a test-tube, we find that the grey zinc powder dissolves, red metallic copper is precipitated, the blue colour of the solution disappears, and heat is evolved. These changes are due to the exothermic reaction

$$Zn + CuSO_4 \rightarrow ZnSO_4 + Cu$$

Because both copper(II) sulphate and zinc sulphate are strong electrolytes, and so can be considered as completely dissociated in solution, we can represent the reaction by the equation

$$Zn + Cu^{2+} \rightarrow Zn^{2+} + Cu$$

The reaction therefore consists simply of the transfer of electrons from zinc metal to copper(II) ions (and of course some associated rearrangement of water molecules for, as we saw in Chapter 3, the zinc and copper(II) ions are both hydrated in solution).

It is possible to devise a galvanic cell in which this same reaction takes place. The reacting substances are not, however, in direct contact with one another but are separated by an electrical conductor, a consequent flow of electrons along this enabling some of the energy of the reaction to be obtained in the form of electrical energy. The cell is known as a *Daniell cell* and is shown diagrammatically in figure 25. A piece of zinc dips into a solution of zinc sulphate and a piece of copper dips into a solution of copper(II) sulphate, the two solutions being kept separate from one another by containing one of them in a porous pot. This enables electrical contact between the solutions to be made, but prevents their becoming mixed. If a voltmeter is placed across the two pieces of metal a voltage will be found to exist between them. The magnitude of this voltage depends on the concentrations of the two solutions: if they are both 1 M the voltage will be about 1 V. Further examination will show that the copper is positively charged and the zinc is negatively charged; consequently, if the two metals are joined by an electrical conductor electrons will flow* along this from the zinc to the copper.

*In the conventional sense *current* flows from positive to negative. This apparently rather misleading convention results from the fact that the properties of an electric current were studied before the discovery of the electron.

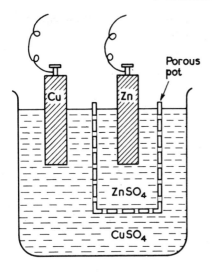

Figure 25 The Daniell cell.

The two pieces of metal are the *electrodes* of the galvanic cell. All galvanic cells contain two electrodes and current flows when they are connected by an electrical conductor. Because electrons travel along this conductor from the negative electrode to the positive electrode, clearly some process is occurring at the former leading to a release of electrons, while at the latter some process must be taking up electrons.

As we saw in Chapter 3, a release of electrons is known as an oxidation reaction and occurs at an anode; a consumption of electrons is known as a reduction reaction and occurs at a cathode. In the Daniell cell the processes taking place are:

at the anode $Zn \rightarrow Zn^{2+} + 2e^-$ (oxidation reaction)

at the cathode $Cu^{2+} + 2e^- \rightarrow Cu$ (reduction reaction)

Electrons must be released and consumed in equal numbers at the two electrodes and the net reaction occurring in the cell is therefore the sum of the two electrode reactions:

$Zn + Cu^{2+} \rightarrow Zn^{2+} + Cu$ (cell reaction)

The force causing the electrons to move around the external circuit is known as the *electromotive force* (e.m.f.). As the electrons pass from anode to cathode the zinc anode dissolves away, thereby increasing the concentration of zinc ions in the surrounding solution, while copper plates out at the cathode, thereby decreasing the local concentration of copper(II) ions. At the same time there is a movement of ions across the porous partition so that the two solutions still contain equivalent numbers of anions and cations (figure 26).

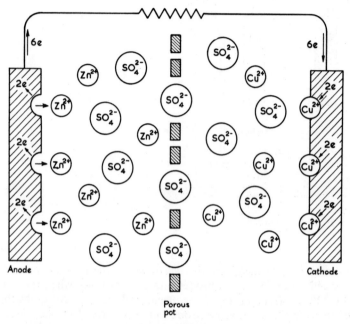

Figure 26 The processes occurring in a Daniell cell. Three zinc atoms are seen dissolving at the anode leading to the release of six electrons. These electrons travel to the cathode where they permit the deposition of three copper atoms. At the same time ions diffuse through the porous pot to preserve the overall electrical neutrality of the solution.

Thermodynamics and galvanic cells

If a Daniell cell is placed in a calorimeter while current is being drawn from it, it will be found that heat is evolved within the cell just as it is in the test-tube reaction. However, the quantities of heat are different in the two cases. In the test-tube reaction the heat evolved is about 212 000 J for each mole of zinc which dissolves. In the galvanic cell the heat evolved is less than this, the balance appearing as electrical work (figure 27). The actual amount of work obtained from the cell depends on the way it is operated. If it were operated under what are known as *thermodynamically reversible conditions* (page 55) the work obtained would be a maximum and equal to about 212 000 J for each mole of zinc dissolving. Such conditions cannot actually be achieved in practical galvanic cells and the net work obtained is always less than this. This maximum might however be thought of as an ideal towards which one might aim in the design of galvanic cells. Thermodynamically reversible cells, however, have some important uses: for example, in the measurement of electrode potentials (Chapter 8) and in the determination of some other important thermodynamic quantities such as heats of reaction and equilibrium constants.

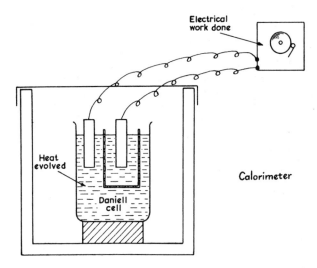

Figure 27 The Daniell cell connected to an electric bell. Part of the energy of the reaction is liberated as heat (and so can be measured in the calorimeter): the remainder appears as electrical energy.

Conventional representation of cells

It is convenient to represent a galvanic cell in some simple conventional fashion. In the case of the Daniell cell we can write it thus

$$Zn|ZnSO_4(1\ M)|CuSO_4(1\ M)|Cu$$

The vertical lines represent boundaries between phases, that is between the metals and the solutions, and between the two solutions. Because the voltage depends on the concentrations of the solutions it is usual to specify these. It is also conventional to write the cell with the negative electrode on the left.

Other galvanic cells

A great many different galvanic cells can be constructed from various electrode materials and electrolyte solutions (see Chapter 8). Although many electrodes consist simply of a piece of metal dipping into a solution containing ions of that metal, it should not be thought that electrodes are exclusively metallic: some important electrodes are based on gases and some on salts. The *hydrogen electrode,* which is very important in connection with the measurement of electrode potentials and in the generation of electricity in *fuel cells* (Chapter 11), consists of a piece of platinum in an acidic solution over which a stream of hydrogen is passed. The electrode reaction occurring is

$$\tfrac{1}{2}H_2 \rightleftharpoons H^+ + e^-$$

the equilibrium sign ($\rightleftharpoons$) indicating that the reaction will go in either direction according to the direction of current flow.

Another important electrode is the silver/silver chloride electrode—a silver wire coated with silver chloride which dips into a solution containing chloride ions. At this electrode the following reaction takes place:

$$AgCl + e^- \rightleftharpoons Ag + Cl^-$$

The hydrogen electrode and the silver/silver chloride electrode can be combined together (figure 28) in the following galvanic cell:

$$Pt,H_2|HCl|AgCl,Ag$$

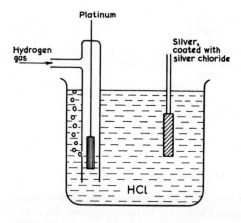

Figure 28 A cell consisting of a hydrogen electrode and a silver/silver chloride electrode.

The measurement of e.m.f.

Although some estimate of the value of the e.m.f. of a cell can be obtained by connecting an ordinary voltmeter across the electrodes this method is inaccurate because the current drawn from the cell by the voltmeter upsets the cell equilibrium and, in consequence, brings about some change in the e.m.f. In a *potentiometer* e.m.f.s are measured in such a way that no current—or only a very little current—is drawn from the cell. A potentiometer may be based on a *valve voltmeter* which operates on a minute current. Alternatively, it may be designed according to the *Poggendorff compensation principle* in which the e.m.f. of the cell under examination is balanced by an equal e.m.f. from another source. The principle is illustrated in figure 29.

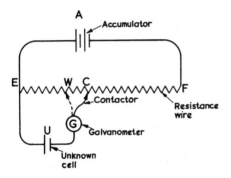

Figure 29 The circuit for the measurement of the e.m.f. of a galvanic cell.

A uniform resistance wire EF is connected to an accumulator A which maintains a uniform fall of potential along the wire. The cell of unknown e.m.f. U is connected as shown so that its e.m.f. opposes that of the accumulator. G is a galvanometer and C is a moving contactor to the resistance wire. C is moved until no current passes through G: the unknown e.m.f. must then be just balanced by the fall of potential between E and C and

$$\frac{\text{e.m.f. of U}}{\text{e.m.f. of A}} = \frac{\text{EC}}{\text{EF}}$$

Measurement of the distances EC and EF enables the unknown e.m.f. to be calculated provided the e.m.f. of the accumulator is known. Because this is not normally known precisely the apparatus is standardized by a *standard cell* which is a carefully constructed cell with a very accurately known e.m.f. One important standard cell is the Weston cell (figure 30). The standard cell replaces the unknown; a balance is obtained as before and if this is at a point W, then

$$\frac{\text{e.m.f. of U}}{\text{e.m.f. of standard}} = \frac{\text{EC}}{\text{EW}}$$

This situation is in fact that envisaged in the concept of a thermodynamically reversible process and the e.m.f. measured is the *thermodynamically reversible e.m.f.* of the cell. As we shall see in Chapter 10, the e.m.f. of a cell measured when a finite current is being drawn from it is not normally equal to the reversible value.

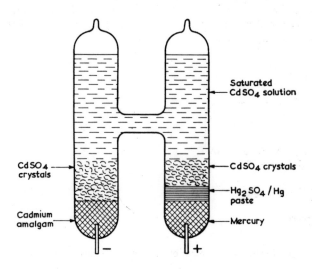

Figure 30 The Weston standard cell.

Example

The method illustrated in figure 29 was used to measure the e.m.f. of the following galvanic cell:

$$Pt,H_2(1 \text{ atm})|HCl(0.1 \text{ M})|AgCl,Ag$$

With this cell in the circuit a balance on the galvanometer was obtained at a point 13.53 cm along the slide wire. When the cell was replaced by a standard Weston cell a balance was obtained at 48.95 cm. The e.m.f. of a Weston cell is 1.018 07 V at 25 °C. What was the e.m.f. of the cell being studied?

Using the equation of page 55 we have

$$\frac{\text{unknown e.m.f.}}{1.018\ 07} = \frac{13.53}{48.95}$$

$$\text{or e.m.f.} = 1.018\ 07 \times \frac{13.53}{48.95} = 0.281\ 5 \text{ V}$$

Cell reactions and electrode polarities

In the study of a galvanic cell it is necessary, as well as measuring the e.m.f. of the cell, to be able to work out the electrode reactions and the overall cell reaction which gives rise to it. This is possible if, when the e.m.f. is being measured, the polarity of the electrodes is also noted. This means observing the way the electrodes of the cell have to be connected to the potentiometer in order to get a balance.

Let us take as an example the cell

$$Pt,H_2|HCl|AgCl,Ag$$

which has just been described. With 1 M HCl the measured e.m.f. will be found to be about 0.2 V. It will also be found that the platinum is the negative electrode and the silver the positive electrode.

The negative polarity of the platinum means that an oxidation reaction (a release of electrons) is taking place there. The electrode reaction must therefore be

$$\tfrac{1}{2}H_2 \rightarrow H^+ + e^-*$$

The positive polarity of the silver means that a reduction reaction (consumption of electrons) is taking place and the electrode reaction must therefore be

$$AgCl + e^- \rightarrow Ag + Cl^-$$

Combining these two electrode reactions gives us the cell reaction

$$AgCl + \tfrac{1}{2}H_2 \rightarrow Ag + HCl$$

Cell reactions should always be quoted along with cell e.m.f.s, for without them the latter have little meaning.

Relationship between cell reaction and e.m.f.

The theoretical relationship between the e.m.f. of a cell and the reaction occurring therein was first studied by Nernst (1864–1941). (The *derivation* of the *Nernst equation* requires the application of thermodynamic principles and will not be given here.)

Let us consider a galvanic cell in which the following hypothetical reaction occurs:

$$aA + bB \rightarrow cC + dD$$

that is, a and b moles respectively of substances A and B react to give c and d moles respectively of C and D. The Nernst equation for the cell then has the following form:

$$E = \frac{RT}{zF} \ln K - \frac{RT}{zF} \ln \left(\frac{[C]^c[D]^d}{[A]^a[B]^b} \right) \tag{7.1}$$

---

*We shall for simplicity write H^+ although, in aqueous solution, the ion will of course be hydrated.

where E denotes the e.m.f. of the cell, R the gas constant, T the temperature, zF the quantity of electricity flowing when a moles of A (or b moles of B etc.) react ($F = 96\ 490\ C\ mol^{-1}$), and K denotes the *equilibrium constant* for the cell reaction. (*Note*. ln refers to natural logarithms (to base e) and the square brackets indicate concentrations.)

It should be noted that equation 7.1 is exact only if the concentrations are replaced by what are known as *activities* (see footnote on page 26).

Equation 7.1 can be simplified to

$$E = E^{\ominus} - \frac{2.303RT}{zF} \lg \left(\frac{[C]^c[D]^d}{[A]^a[B]^b} \right) \tag{7.2}$$

where $E^{\ominus} = (RT/zF) \ln K$ and is known as the *standard e.m.f. of the cell*. It is the value of the e.m.f. when all the concentrations (strictly the activities) in the logarithmic term are equal to unity (since $\lg 1 = 0$). The equation can be further simplified for a temperature of 25 °C to

$$E = E^{\ominus} - \frac{0.059}{z} \lg \left(\frac{[C]^c[D]^d}{[A]^a[B]^b} \right) \tag{7.3}$$

by substituting the appropriate values of R, F, and T (298 K).

Cell e.m.f.s and Gibbs free energies

It can be shown that the e.m.f. of a cell is related to the Gibbs free energy change, ΔG, for the reaction taking place in the cell. Under reversible conditions the decrease in the Gibbs free energy of the cell is equal to the amount of electrical work done. This latter can be shown to equal $\int EI\,dt$ where I is the current flowing, the integration being performed over the time (t) for which the current is flowing. If the quantity of electricity obtained from the cell is zF, then

$$\int_{t=0}^{t=t} EI\,dt = E \int_{t=0}^{t=t} I\,dt = zFE \text{ or } \Delta G = -zFE.$$

Under standard conditions, similarly,

$$\Delta G^{\ominus} = -zFE^{\ominus}$$

Measured values of the e.m.f.s of cells can therefore be used to obtain ΔG values for chemical reactions; electrochemical cells are consequently a valuable source of thermodynamic data.

Applications of the Nernst equation

If the relevant concentration terms for the hydrogen/silver chloride cell are inserted into equation 7.1 we obtain

$$E = \frac{RT \ln K}{zF} - \frac{RT}{zF} \ln \frac{[Ag][HCl]}{[AgCl][H_2]^{\frac{1}{2}}}$$

Now, silver and silver chloride are both solids and their mass concentrations are the same as their densities. These are constant at constant temperature and so can be taken out and incorporated into the constant first term of the equation. Note also that we do not usually measure the *concentrations* of gases but prefer to use *pressures* (which are proportional to concentrations). For the reaction of one mole of silver chloride (or one half mole of hydrogen), z is one and the Nernst equation therefore becomes

$$E = E^\ominus - \frac{2.303RT}{F} \lg \frac{[HCl]}{p_{H_2}{}^{\frac{1}{2}}}$$

where p_{H_2} is the pressure of hydrogen in atmospheres.

Example
Calculate the e.m.f. of the following cell at 25 °C:

$$Pt,H_2|HCl|AgCl,Ag$$

when the pressure of hydrogen gas equals 1 atm and the concentration of hydrochloric acid is (*i*) 0.1 M, (*ii*) 0.01 M, and (*iii*) 0.001 M. The standard e.m.f. of the cell is 0.223 V.

Using the Nernst equation

$$E = E^\ominus - \frac{2.303RT}{F} \lg \frac{[HCl]}{p_{H_2}{}^{\frac{1}{2}}}$$

We have

$$E = 0.223 - 0.059 \lg [HCl]$$

Substituting for the different HCl concentrations gives the following values for E:

HCl concentration	E/V
0.1 M	0.282
0.01 M	0.341
0.001 M	0.400

Liquid junction potentials

For the Daniell cell the Nernst equation cannot be written down in any simple fashion because of the existence of what are known as *liquid junction potentials*. These arise in cells in which there is a boundary between two different liquid phases and are caused by diffusion processes occurring at such a boundary. In the Daniell cell, zinc ions can diffuse into the copper(II) sulphate solution and copper(II) ions can diffuse into the zinc sulphate solution at the porous pot where the two solutions meet. Liquid junction potentials cannot be calculated by the Nernst equation.

Fortunately, they are usually small and can often be almost completely eliminated by using a *salt bridge* to connect the two solutions. Salt bridges are commonly made from a saturated solution of potassium chloride (figure 31). The salt bridge creates *two* liquid junctions, the potentials of which are determined almost completely by the diffusion of potassium chloride. They are both equal in magnitude therefore, but act in opposite directions thereby cancelling each other out.

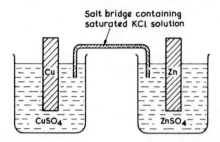

Figure 31 A Daniell cell containing a salt bridge.

For the Daniell cell with a salt bridge the Nernst equation becomes

$$E = E^{\ominus} - \frac{2.303RT}{zF} \lg \frac{[Zn^{2+}]}{[Cu^{2+}]}$$

z being equal to two for each mole of zinc dissolved.

Problems

1 The Poggendorff method was used for measuring the e.m.f. of the following cell at 25 °C:

$$Co|Co^{2+} (1\ M)||Cu^{2+} (1\ M)|Cu*$$

With a standard Weston cell (e.m.f. = 1.018 07 V) in the circuit a balance was obtained at 50.9 cm. With the cell under examination a balance was obtained at 30.85 cm. Calculate the e.m.f. of the cell.

2 Use the Nernst equation to calculate the e.m.f. at 25 °C of the following cell:

$$Zn|ZnCl_2 (0.1\ M)|Cl_2 (1.2\ atm), Pt$$

The standard e.m.f. of the cell is 2.12 V and the reaction taking place in it is:

$$Zn + Cl_2 \rightarrow Zn^{2+} + 2Cl^-$$

*The double line between the solutions denotes that they are connected by means of a salt bridge.

Electrode Potentials 8

A galvanic cell, as we have seen, is a device for converting the energy of a chemical reaction into electrical energy. In the Daniell cell the reaction is

$$Cu^{2+} + Zn \rightarrow Cu + Zn^{2+}$$

part of the energy of the reaction appearing as electrical energy and part appearing as heat.

The equation for the overall reaction can be broken down into equations for the separate electrode reactions

at the anode $\quad Zn \rightarrow Zn^{2+} + 2e^-$
at the cathode $Cu^{2+} + 2e^- \rightarrow Cu$

In a similar way it is possible to break down the e.m.f. of the cell into two separate *electrode potentials*, one for the anode and one for the cathode. To understand this let us consider in more detail the processes that we should expect to take place at the electrodes.

First, let us separate the cell into two halves so that we have one *half-cell* consisting of a copper electrode dipping into a solution of copper(II) sulphate and another half-cell consisting of a zinc electrode dipping into a solution of zinc sulphate (figure 32). Let us assume that the two electrodes are perfectly clean and not contaminated by a surface film of oxide or other material. The normal Daniell cell reaction cannot now take place of course because the two halves of the cell are not in electrical contact. Nevertheless, in the copper half-cell there is still a *tendency* for copper ions to deposit from the solution on to the electrode (an *ion discharge* reaction); at the same time there is also a *tendency* for the copper electrode to dissolve into the solution as copper(II) ions (an *ionization* reaction). The relative importance of these two processes depends on

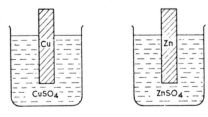

Figure 32 The Daniell cell separated into two half-cells.

the concentration of the copper(II) sulphate solution. If this concentration is high the discharge process should predominate over the solution process. (In a concentrated solution more copper(II) ions tend to deposit out.) If the concentration is low the ionization process should predominate. However, neither process can take place to more than a very minute extent. In a concentrated solution the discharge of a few excess copper(II) ions gives rise to a positive charge on the metal which repels copper(II) ions from the surface and so prevents any further deposition. In a sufficiently dilute solution a small excess of copper(II) ions going into solution leaves a negative charge on the metal which prevents further ionization. In a solution of some intermediate concentration the two processes take place to similar extents. In all cases a state of equilibrium is reached* leading to a separation of charge between the solution and the metal. The position of equilibrium is such that in the more concentrated solution there is an excess of positive charge on the metal and an excess of negative charge in the solution. In the more dilute solution there is an excess of negative charge on the metal and an excess of positive charge on the solution.

It would be very convenient if we could measure a potential difference between a metal and the solution arising out of these charge separations. Unfortunately this cannot be done. There would be an obvious practical difficulty if we were to attempt to do this by means of an ordinary potentiometer. The metal electrode could be easily connected to the potentiometer by means of a wire: attempting to connect the solution would mean introducing a wire into it which would act simply as another electrode and would acquire its own characteristic potential. The potentiometer would then simply measure a potential difference between two electrodes which would not be the same as that between electrode and solution. There is also another difficulty which prevents more sophisticated methods being used. This is that the theory of electrostatics only allows a potential difference to be *defined* between two points in a *single* phase. We need not pursue this further but must simply accept that potential differences between metal and solution are not measurable.

Let us now turn our attention to the other half of the Daniell cell, that consisting of the zinc electrode dipping into the zinc sulphate solution. Now, clearly we should expect the same kinds of processes to be taking place here as at the copper electrode, zinc ions dissolving from the electrode and also being deposited on to the electrode from the solution. However, zinc has different properties from copper and we should not expect these processes to take place to the same extent. The position of equilibrium in consequence will be different and the potential of the zinc will not be the same as that of the copper. Hence, in the complete Daniell

*This is a state of *dynamic* equilibrium, there being a continuous exchange of ions between the electrode and the solution.

cell, with the two solutions now in electrical contact, there will exist a difference of potential between the two electrodes. This is the cell e.m.f. and can be measured by the method described in Chapter 7.

Standard electrode potentials

If we had been able to measure the potentials of our single electrodes then the measured cell e.m.f. would be equal to the difference of these *single electrode potentials*.* A table of single electrode potentials would be very useful, enabling the ready calculation of the e.m.f.s of cells constructed from any two half-cells to be carried out. As such a table is unfortunately impossible to obtain we fall back on the expedient of constructing a table of *relative potentials*, that is, electrode potentials measured *relative* to some standard electrode. The standard electrode chosen is the hydrogen electrode (page 54). With the hydrogen gas at a pressure of 101 325 N m^{-2} (one atmosphere) and the solution at a concentration of 1 M (strictly at unit activity), the electrode is *defined* as having a *standard electrode potential* of zero. This value, it should be emphasized, is not the result of any measurement. It is purely a defined, or conventional, value.

If we now combine this hydrogen electrode with first the copper half-cell and then the zinc half-cell it is possible to measure similar conventional potentials for copper and zinc (provided of course that we take precautions to eliminate the liquid junction potentials). When these measurements are made on half-cells in which the concentration of the solution is 1 M (strictly, unit activity) these potentials are known as the *standard electrode potentials* of the metals.

If, for example, we construct the following galvanic cell

$$Pt,H_2|HCl\ (1\ M)||CuSO_4\ (1\ M)|Cu$$

and measure the potential difference between the electrodes then, since one of these is defined as having a zero standard electrode potential, it is a simple matter to obtain the standard electrode potential of the other. We must first decide however whether to use the expression

$$E^{\ominus}_{cell} = E^{\ominus}_{Cu} - E^{\ominus}_{H_2} \tag{8.1}$$

or

$$E^{\ominus}_{cell} = E^{\ominus}_{H_2} - E^{\ominus}_{Cu} \tag{8.2}$$

where $E^{\ominus}_{cell}$ is the measured standard e.m.f. of the cell and $E^{\ominus}_{H_2}$ and $E^{\ominus}_{Cu}$ are the standard electrode potentials of the hydrogen and copper

---

*This is assuming that there is no potential difference between the two solutions at the point of contact; there is normally a junction potential but as was explained in Chapter 7 special techniques enable this to be eliminated or at least minimized.

electrodes. There is no overriding reason why we should choose one in preference to the other although the different choices would give rise to different *signs* for the electrode potential of the copper. The measured e.m.f. of the cell is found to be 0.34 V. Using this value with equation 8.1 gives

$$0.34 = E_{Cu}^{\ominus} - 0$$

or

$$E_{Cu}^{\ominus} = +0.34 \text{ V}$$

On the other hand, using the e.m.f. with equation 8.2 gives

$$0.34 = 0 - E_{Cu}^{\ominus}$$

or

$$E_{Cu}^{\ominus} = -0.34 \text{ V}$$

Clearly, it is necessary to adopt a particular convention.

In the cell the overall reaction taking place is

$$Cu^{2+} + H_2 \rightarrow Cu + 2H^+$$

or writing the two half-cell reactions separately

$$Cu^{2+} + 2e^- \rightarrow Cu$$
$$H_2 \rightarrow 2H^+ + 2e^-$$

The reaction taking place at the copper electrode is a *reduction* reaction (since it involves the taking up of electrons) and we call the standard electrode potential of this electrode a *reduction potential*.

When we turn to the cell consisting of a zinc half-cell and a hydrogen half-cell we encounter a rather different situation. The measured e.m.f. of the cell is 0.76 V, but the reaction taking place is

$$2H^+ + Zn \rightarrow H_2 + Zn^{2+}$$

the two half-cell reactions being:

$$Zn \rightarrow Zn^{2+} + 2e^-$$
$$2H^+ + 2e^- \rightarrow H_2$$

In this cell an *oxidation* reaction takes place at the zinc electrode and not a reduction reaction. Clearly, it would not be very sensible to list reduction potentials for some metals and oxidation potentials for others. A simple rule is that the e.m.f. of a galvanic cell equals the electrode potential of the cathode minus the electrode potential of the anode when both are written as reduction potentials:

$$E(\text{cell}) = E(\text{cathode}) - E(\text{anode})$$

In the case of the two cells just considered we should then have:

(a) for Cu $\quad E^{\ominus}_{cell} = E^{\ominus}_{Cu} - E^{\ominus}_{H_2}$

$\qquad\qquad 0.34 = E^{\ominus}_{Cu} - 0$

$\qquad\qquad E^{\ominus}_{Cu} = 0.34$ V

(b) for Zn $\quad E^{\ominus}_{cell} = E^{\ominus}_{H_2} - E^{\ominus}_{Zn}$

$\qquad\qquad 0.76 = 0 - E^{\ominus}_{Zn}$

$\qquad\qquad E^{\ominus}_{Zn} = -0.76$ V

and these give us the *reduction potentials* of the two electrodes.

It has been the practice in the past for some workers (particularly in the USA) to quote oxidation potentials rather than reduction potentials and this has sometimes led to some confusion. The situation has been clarified somewhat in recent years by the more widespread adoption of the *International Convention on Electrode Potentials* which recommends the use of reduction potentials. The situation is, however, rather complex and some care is necessary if the student is to be able to perform calculations correctly. The treatment given here is somewhat simplified: a more detailed treatment would require more understanding of the principles of thermodynamics and is beyond the scope of this book.

Some standard electrode potentials (reduction potentials) are given in table 11. It should be emphasized that these values are all relative values,

Electrode*	$E^{\ominus}/V$
Li^+/Li	−3.05
Rb^+/Rb	−2.93
K^+/K	−2.93
Cs^+/Cs	−2.92
Ca^{2+}/Ca	−2.87
Na^+/Na	−2.71
Mg^{2+}/Mg	−2.37
Zn^{2+}/Zn	−0.76
Fe^{2+}/Fe	−0.44
Cd^{2+}/Cd	−0.40
Ni^{2+}/Ni	−0.25
Pb^{2+}/Pb	−0.13
H^+/H_2	0
Cu^{2+}/Cu	+0.34
$OH^-/O_2, H_2O$	+0.40
Cu^+/Cu	+0.52
Ag^+/Ag	+0.80
Hg^{2+}/Hg	+0.85
Cl_2/Cl^-	+1.36

Table 11 Standard electrode potentials (aqueous solutions at 25 °C).

*This indicates the reduction reaction associated with the value quoted, e.g. $Li^+ + e^- \rightarrow Li$ is represented Li^+/Li. To be strictly consistent with convention this should be written as a subscript to the symbol for electrode potential, that is, for example $E_{Cu^{2+}/Cu}$.

based on the convention that $E_{H_2}^{\ominus} = 0$. The standard hydrogen electrode is normally used as the basis of electrode potential measurements although other electrodes could be—and sometimes are—used. If a different standard were used then the values of electrode potentials would be changed: however, their relative values would be unaltered and values for the e.m.f.s of galvanic cells would remain the same.

Example

The e.m.f. of the cell

$$Cd|CdSO_4(1\ M)||HCl(1\ M)|H_2,Pt$$

was found to be 0.40 V, the cadmium electrode being the negative electrode. Write down (*a*) the reactions occurring at the electrodes and (*b*) the overall cell reaction. Calculate the standard potential of the cadmium electrode.

Since the cadmium electrode is negative a release of electrons must be taking place there:

$$Cd \rightarrow Cd^{2+} + 2e^-$$

This is an oxidation reaction and the cadmium electrode is therefore the anode. The hydrogen electrode is positive and the reduction reaction

$$2H^+ + 2e^- \rightarrow H_2$$

must therefore be taking place, this electrode being the cathode.

The cell reaction is the sum of the electrode reactions

$$Cd + 2H^+ \rightarrow Cd^{2+} + H_2$$

(This, of course, is also the equation for the reaction which takes place when cadmium is added to hydrochloric acid in a test-tube.)

The standard potential of the cadmium electrode is obtained from the expression

$$E(\text{cell}) = E(\text{cathode}) - E(\text{anode})$$

or

$$0.40 = E_{H_2}^{\ominus} - E_{Cd}^{\ominus}$$

$E_{H_2}^{\ominus}$ is zero by definition and hence

$$E_{Cd}^{\ominus} = -0.40\ V$$

Secondary standard electrodes

Although the hydrogen electrode is the standard of our electrode potential scale, it is an electrode which is not always very convenient or simple to use. It is common, therefore, to use certain secondary standards, two of which are the silver chloride electrode (described on page 54) and the calomel electrode (figure 33). The standard potentials of these electrodes are known very accurately from prior measurements against a hydrogen electrode: these potentials can then be used in subsequent measurements. The calomel electrode is particularly simple to construct and gives accurately reproducible values of its electrode potential.

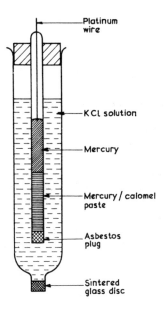

Figure 33 The calomel electrode.

The calomel electrode consists of a platinum wire dipping into pure mercury which rests on a paste made of a mixture of calomel (mercury(I) chloride) and mercury. This paste is in contact with a solution of potassium chloride which acts as a salt bridge to the other half of the cell. The potential of the electrode depends on the concentration of the potassium chloride solution. It is usually most convenient to use a saturated solution and the potential at 25 °C is then 0.244 4 V.

The calomel electrode is generally used as the standard electrode in the measurement of pH with the glass electrode (see page 73).

Example
In order to measure the standard electrode potential of the tin (Sn^{2+}) electrode, this was combined with a calomel electrode to form the cell:

$Sn|SnCl_2(1 \text{ M})|KCl(\text{sat.})|Hg_2Cl_2,Hg$

The tin electrode was found to be the negative electrode. The measured e.m.f. of the cell was 0.385 V. What was the standard electrode potential of the tin electrode?

Since the tin electrode constitutes the anode of the cell we have

$$E(\text{cell}) = E_{\text{ca1}} - E_{\text{Sn}}^{\ominus}$$

or

$$0.385 = 0.244 - E_{\text{Sn}}^{\ominus}$$

Hence

$$E_{\text{Sn}}^{\ominus} = -0.141 \text{ V}$$

The influence of electrolyte concentration on electrode potential

Let us return to the half-cell consisting of a copper electrode in a solution of copper(II) sulphate. We saw that at equilibrium there was a balance between ions going into solution from the metal and ions being deposited from solution on to the metal. If the concentration of copper(II) sulphate in the solution is *increased* more positive copper(II) ions will be deposited on to the electrode before a new balance point is struck. At this new point of equilibrium the electrode potential will be *more positive* than it was before. If, on the other hand, the copper(II) sulphate solution is made *more dilute*, more copper(II) ions will go into solution before a balance is reached. In this case the electrode potential will be *less positive* than before. In other words, increasing the concentration of copper(II) ions increases the electrode potential; decreasing the concentration of copper(II) ions decreases the electrode potential.

Precisely the same thing will be true of the zinc/zinc sulphate half-cell. The fact that the standard reduction potential of zinc is negative whereas that for copper is positive makes no difference. These two (conventional) values only indicate that the balance points in 1 M solution are different.

The relationship between electrode potential and metal ion concentration is given by the *Nernst equation for a single electrode*. For copper this is

$$E_{\text{Cu}} = E_{\text{Cu}}^{\ominus} + \frac{2.303RT}{zF} \lg [\text{Cu}^{2+}] \tag{8.3}$$

where E_{Cu} denotes the electrode potential in a solution of concentration $[\text{Cu}^{2+}]$, $E_{\text{Cu}}^{\ominus}$ the standard electrode potential (concentration 1 M), and z the number of electrons released in the ionization of one copper atom ($z = 2$). For zinc the equation is

$$E_{\text{Zn}} = E_{\text{Zn}}^{\ominus} + \frac{2.303RT}{zF} \lg [\text{Zn}^{2+}] \tag{8.4}$$

A study of the last two equations shows that they both correctly indicate that increasing metal ion concentration leads, for copper, to increasingly positive electrode potential and, for zinc, to increasingly less negative electrode potential.

The copper and zinc electrodes are both electrodes which are reversible to cations; that is, their potentials result from a balance between deposition and ionization of positive ions. Some important electrodes are, however, reversible to anions. If chlorine gas is bubbled over a platinum electrode the platinum acquires a potential as a result of the reaction

$$\tfrac{1}{2}Cl_2 + e^- \rightarrow Cl^-$$

Such an electrode (the chlorine electrode) is similar to the hydrogen electrode. Its potential depends, however, on the pressure of chlorine gas and on the concentration in solution of chloride ions.

If we take any such anion reversible electrode and *increase* the concentration of anions, the electrode potential *decreases*. In the case of the chlorine electrode ($z = 1$) the Nernst equation is therefore

$$E_{Cl_2} = E_{Cl_2}^{\ominus} - \frac{2.303RT}{F} \lg \left(\frac{[Cl^-]}{p_{Cl_2}^{\frac{1}{2}}} \right) \tag{8.5}$$

For the silver/silver chloride electrode ($z = 1$) it is

$$E_{AgCl} = E_{AgCl}^{\ominus} - \frac{2.303RT}{F} \lg [Cl^-] \tag{8.6}$$

Although these two electrodes both respond to the same anion their electrode potentials are different—even if $p_{Cl_2} = 1$—because the values of $E_{Cl_2}^{\ominus}$ and E_{AgCl} are different.

Comparing equations 8.3 and 8.4 with 8.5 and 8.6 we see that the first two contain a plus sign and the latter two a minus sign. These signs are *intuitively* correct since they predict the obvious way in which electrode potential responds to changes in the concentration of the ion to which the electrode is responsive. An electrode which responds to positive ions in solution becomes more positive (or less negative) as the concentration of those ions is increased; an electrode which responds to negative ions in solution becomes less positive (or more negative) when the concentration of those negative ions is increased.

However, these two forms of the Nernst equation are also *formally consistent* with each other and also with the Nernst equation for the complete cell, which was given in equation 7.3, provided that the following rule is adopted:

the Nernst equation is always written with a *minus* sign
(i) for a cell reaction when the reaction occurring in the cell is a spontaneous one (e.g. for the Daniell cell, $Cu^{2+} + Zn \rightarrow Cu + Zn^{2+}$)
(ii) for an electrode reaction when that reaction is written as a *reduction* reaction.

For a copper electrode the reduction reaction is

$$Cu^{2+} + 2e^- \rightarrow Cu$$

and the formal Nernst equation would be

$$E = E^\ominus - \frac{RT}{2F} \ln \frac{[Cu]}{[Cu^{2+}]}$$

However, copper being a solid and hence having a constant concentration (or more formally having an activity of unity) the equation can be simplified to

$$E = E^\ominus - \frac{RT}{2F} \ln \frac{1}{[Cu^{2+}]}$$

$$= E^\ominus + \frac{RT}{2F} \ln [Cu^{2+}]$$

which is equation 8.3 (with $z = 2$).

An exactly similar relationship can be derived for the zinc electrode. For the chlorine and silver chloride electrodes a similar treatment leads to equations 8.5 and 8.6 which the reader may care to confirm for himself.

In this way formal rules can be laid down for establishing the correct application of the Nernst equation to cell and electrode reactions. However a detailed description of these would mean going beyond the qualitative approach of this book and so will not be attempted here.

Example

The e.m.f. of the cell

$$Hg,Hg_2Cl_2|KCl(1\ M)|Cl_2(p = 1.13\ atm),Pt$$

was found to be 1.092 V, the calomel electrode being the negative electrode. The potential of the 1 M calomel electrode is 0.268 V.* What is the standard potential of the chlorine electrode?

From the expression

$$E(\text{cell}) = E(\text{cathode}) - E(\text{anode})$$

we have

$$1.092 = E_{Cl_2} - 0.268$$

or

$$E_{Cl_2} = 1.360\ V$$

This, however, is not the standard electrode potential which must be

*Note the difference between this figure and that quoted on page 67. The latter, however, relates to the electrode containing a *saturated* potassium chloride solution.

calculated from the Nernst equation:

$$E_{Cl_2} = E_{Cl_2}^{\ominus} - 0.059 \lg \left(\frac{[Cl^-]}{p_{ce_2}^{\frac{1}{2}}}\right)$$

or

$$1.360 = E_{Cl_2}^{\ominus} - 0.059 \lg \frac{1}{1.13^{\frac{1}{2}}}$$

which gives

$$E_{Cl_2}^{\ominus} = 1.360 + 0.059 \lg \frac{1}{1.13^{\frac{1}{2}}}$$

$$= 1.358 \text{ V}$$

The electrochemical series

It is very useful to have a table of standard electrode potentials: this is sometimes known as the *electrochemical* series. Such values, used with the appropriate Nernst equations, enable the calculation of the e.m.f.s of cells, constructed from any appropriate pair of half-cells, to be carried out. The table is, however, of somewhat more general use. If it is drawn up in order of standard electrode potentials with, as is usual, the most negative potentials at the top (table 11), then the table indicates a general order of reactivity of the elements. The alkali metals, which are the most reactive metals, are found at the top of the table; the noble metals, which are exceptionally unreactive, appear near the bottom.

The position of an element, relative to the position of hydrogen, indicates whether that element tends to replace hydrogen from solution, that is, if it dissolves in acids with the evolution of hydrogen. Zinc, which appears above hydrogen, does this; copper, which appears below hydrogen, does not.

However, one must use some caution in this approach for it is very easy to draw conclusions which are not in accordance with experimental observations. Firstly, we should note that 'reactivity' does not have any precise meaning: we should not expect exactly the same order for different kinds of reaction. For example, although the alkali metals, which all react with water, appear at the top of the table, the table order does not indicate the order of such reactivities, the reaction of potassium with water being much more violent than that of lithium. The figures relate strictly only to equilibrium conditions (and can then be used to make predictions about these) but other factors have to be taken into account if reactions are to be accurately predicted. Much of the study of reaction kinetics and chemical thermodynamics is concerned with these factors.

It should also be noted that the table lists only the $E^{\ominus}$ values, that is, the potentials in 1 M solution. If the concentration of ions is very much less than 1 M then the actual electrode potential differs appreciably from the standard value and this can have some important consequences. For example, although the alkali metals dissolve readily both in acids and in water, metals lower down the series dissolve only in acids. In 0.1 M HCl the hydronium ion concentration is 1×10^{-1} mol dm^{-3}, whereas in pure water it is 1×10^{-7} mol dm^{-3}. The term

$$\frac{2.303RT}{zF} \lg [H_3O^+]$$

in the acid solution is equal to -0.059 V but in water it is -0.414 V: for the metal cadmium, therefore, with an $E^\ominus$ value of -0.40 V, the metal and hydrogen retain their relative positions in 0.1 M HCl. Cadmium therefore displaces hydrogen from this acid. In water, however, the positions are reversed and consequently cadmium does not react with water. Accurate calculations are not possible, however, because of *overpotential* effects (Chapter 10).

The presence of overpotential can be responsible for some apparent anomalies in the table. Although lead appears above hydrogen, nevertheless it does not dissolve in acids owing to the fact that the reaction

$$H^+ + e^- \rightarrow \tfrac{1}{2}H_2$$

takes place only with considerable difficulty on the surface of lead.

Another point that must be remembered is that the electrochemical series in table 11 lists potentials in aqueous solutions. In other solvents potentials will be different, not only in magnitude but also with regard to order. Table 12 lists some potentials in other solvents from which some variation in relative position can be seen. Nevertheless, the electrochemical series can be a useful guide to chemical behaviour provided that sufficient care is taken in drawing conclusions from it.

Electrode	Solvent: H_2O $E^\ominus/V$	NH_3 $E^\ominus/V$	CH_3CN $E^\ominus/V$
Li$^+$/Li	−3.05	−2.24	−3.23
Rb$^+$/Rb	−2.93	−1.93	−3.17
K$^+$/K	−2.93	−1.98	−3.16
Cs$^+$/Cs	−2.92	−1.95	−3.16
Ca^{2+}/Ca	−2.87	−1.74	−2.75
Na$^+$/Na	−2.71	−1.85	−2.87
Zn^{2+}/Zn	−0.76	−0.53	−0.74
Cd^{2+}/Cd	−0.40	−0.20	−0.47
Pb^{2+}/Pb	−0.13	+0.32	−0.12
H$^+$/H$_2$*	0	0	0
Cu^{2+}/Cu	+0.34	+0.43	−0.28
Ag$^+$/Ag	+0.80	+0.83	+0.23

Table 12 Standard electrode potentials in different solvents.

*H_3O^+/H$_2$ in water; NH$_4$$^+$/H$_2$ in ammonia; CH$_4$CN$^+$/H$_2$ in ethanonitrile.

The glass electrode

If two acid solutions of different concentrations are separated by a thin glass membrane a potential difference is established between the two sides of the glass. If the concentration of one solution is kept constant and the other is varied it is found that the potential difference changes in response to this variation.

This phenomenon permits the construction of a glass electrode which is responsive to hydrogen ions (figure 34). This consists normally of a thin glass bulb containing 0.1 M hydrochloric acid together with a silver/silver chloride electrode, the bulb being sealed from the atmosphere.

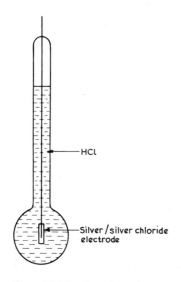

Figure 34 The glass electrode.

The electrode develops a potential when it is inserted into an acid solution the value of which (relative to the standard hydrogen electrode) can be measured by the usual potentiometric techniques. The precise relationship between the potential and the acidity is complex and cannot be discussed in detail here. It can, however, normally be written as

$$E = E_g^\ominus - \frac{2.303RT}{F}(\text{pH})$$

This electrode therefore enables measurements of the pH of solutions to be made and overcomes to some extent the difficulties that were discussed on page 38.

The glass electrode is very simple to use. It is unaffected by oxidizing and reducing agents and by common electrode poisons such as arsenic and sulphur compounds all of which tend to upset the normal functioning of the hydrogen electrode. It is frequently used in conjunction with a special potentiometer known as a pH meter.

The glass electrode is one example of an important class of electrodes known as *ion-selective electrodes*. A number of these have been developed in recent years and are now of great importance in chemistry, biology and medicine.

Problems

1 Using the results of problem 1, Chapter 7, calculate the standard potential of the cobalt electrode. In the cell referred to, the copper electrode was the positive electrode.

2 Devise a galvanic cell in which the following reaction would occur:

$$Mg + Ni^{2+} \rightarrow Mg^{2+} + Ni$$

Calculate the standard e.m.f. of the cell and write down the anode and cathode reactions.

3 An electrode consisting of an iron wire in a solution of $FeCl_2$ is combined with a saturated calomel electrode to give a galvanic cell. Write down the conventional representation for the cell. Calculate the e.m.f. of the cell at 25 °C when the $FeCl_2$ solution is 0.15 M. Write down the reactions occurring at the anode and cathode and the overall cell reaction.

Electron Transfer Reactions $\quad$ 9

Most of the electrodes that we have discussed so far have been what are known as *active electrodes*; that is they have been electrodes which participate in a reaction at the interface between the electrode and the surrounding solution (page 20). However, some electrodes are chemically inert and serve only to *transfer electrons* between the species involved in the reaction. In the hydrogen half-cell, for example, the chemical reaction taking place is

$$\tfrac{1}{2}H_2 + H_2O \rightleftharpoons H_3O^+ + e^-$$

but the platinum electrode does not participate in this reaction other than by transferring electrons between the species H_3O^+ and H_2.

In a solution containing both iron(ii) and iron(iii) ions the reactions

$$Fe^{2+} \rightarrow Fe^{3+} + e^- \quad \text{(oxidation)} \tag{9.1}$$

and

$$Fe^{3+} + e^- \rightarrow Fe^{2+} \quad \text{(reduction)} \tag{9.2}$$

can both take place on the surface of a platinum electrode. If, therefore, a platinum wire is immersed in such a solution it will acquire a potential, the magnitude of which will be given by the relative amounts of iron(ii) and iron(iii) ions present. If there is a sufficient excess of iron(ii) ion the potential will be negative (reaction 9.1). If there is a sufficient excess of iron(iii) ion the potential will be positive (reaction 9.2).

This potential is known as a *redox potential* because it results from the *red*uction or *ox*idation of different ions of the same metal. The magnitude of the redox potential is given by the corresponding Nernst equation which, in this case, is

$$E = E^{\ominus} - 2.303 \frac{RT}{F} \lg \frac{[Fe^{2+}]}{[Fe^{3+}]}$$

The standard redox potential, $E^{\ominus}$, corresponds to the potential acquired by the platinum electrode when it is immersed in a solution containing equal concentrations (strictly, activities) of iron(ii) and iron(iii) ions. It should be noted that in this it differs from the $E^{\ominus}$ values that we have defined previously.

A solution containing tin(ii) and tin(iv) ions behaves in a similar way to an iron(ii)/iron(iii) ion solution. A platinum electrode immersed in it acquires a potential, the value of which is given by the equation

$$E = E^{\ominus} - 2.303 \frac{RT}{2F} \lg \frac{[Sn^{2+}]}{[Sn^{4+}]}$$

The general Nernst equation for any such oxidation–reduction process is

$$E = E^{\ominus} - 2.303 \frac{RT}{zF} \lg \frac{[red]}{[ox]}$$

where [red] is the concentration of the reduced form and [ox] is the concentration of the oxidized form. Such processes are often known as *redox processes*, the electrodes being known as *redox electrodes*.

Measurements of redox potentials have many important applications, particularly in analytical chemistry. An important technique based upon redox principles is known as *polarography*: this uses an electrode consisting of a stream of mercury drops issuing from a capillary into the solution under test. The surface of the electrode is by this means kept perfectly clean and free from products resulting from the oxidation or reduction processes taking place. By varying the potential applied to the

Reaction	$E^{\ominus}/V$
$Cr^{3+} + e^- \rightarrow Cr^{2+}$	-0.408
$Ti^{3+} + e^- \rightarrow Ti^{2+}$	-0.369
$V^{3+} + e^- \rightarrow V^{2+}$	-0.256
$CO_2 + 2H^+ + 2e^- \rightarrow HCO_2H$	-0.199
$Sn^{4+} + 2e^- \rightarrow Sn^{2+}$	$+0.15$
$Cu^{2+} + e^- \rightarrow Cu^+$	$+0.153$
$Fe(CN)_6{}^{3-} + e^- \rightarrow Fe(CN)_6{}^{4-}$	$+0.36$
$C_2H_2 + 2H^+ + 2e^- \rightarrow C_2H_4$	$+0.731$
$Fe^{3+} + e^- \rightarrow Fe^{2+}$	$+0.771$
$Cr_2O^{2-}{}_7 + 14H^+ + 6e^- \rightarrow 2Cr^{3+} + 7H_2O$	$+1.33$
$Mn^{3+} + e^- \rightarrow Mn^{2+}$	$+1.51$
$MnO_4{}^- + 8H^+ + 5e^- \rightarrow Mn^{2+} + 4H_2O$	$+1.52$
$H_2O_2 + 2H^+ + 2e^- \rightarrow 2H_2O$	$+1.776$

Table 13 Some oxidation–reduction potentials in acidic aqueous solutions at 25 °C.

mercury electrode and measuring the resulting current passing through the solution, much useful information can be obtained. The concentrations of metal ions, for example, can be readily and accurately determined, even when several different ions are present in the solution.

A table of standard redox potentials (table 13) lists, in effect, the relative oxidizing powers of oxidizing agents. The permanganate ion in acidic solution oxidizes (and is itself reduced) by the reaction

$$MnO_4{}^- + 8H^+ + 5e^- \rightarrow Mn^{2+} + 4H_2O$$

The redox potential associated with this reaction is $E^{\ominus} = +1.52$ V. For the iron(III) ion the reaction is

$$Fe^{3+} + e^- \rightarrow Fe^{2+}$$

the associated standard redox potential being $E^{\ominus} = +0.771$ V. These two figures show that under standard conditions the permanganate ion is a more powerful oxidizing agent than the iron(III) ion. If, therefore, two solutions, each containing equivalent concentrations of the ions of the redox systems, are mixed, the iron(II) ion will be oxidized by the permanganate ion.

Examples

(i) A 1 M solution of $CrCl_2$ is added to a 1 M solution of $FeCl_3$. Will any oxidation–reduction reaction take place?

We are here concerned with the possibility of the reaction

$$Fe^{3+} + Cr^{2+} \rightarrow Fe^{2+} + Cr^{3+}$$

For the reaction

$$Fe^{3+} + e^- \rightarrow Fe^{2+}$$

the redox potential (from table 13) is $+0.771$ V. For the reaction

$$Cr^{3+} + e^- \rightarrow Cr^{2+}$$

the redox potential is -0.408 V.

If a galvanic cell were constructed from two redox electrodes at which these reactions could take place, clearly the $Fe^{3+}|Fe^{2+}$ electrode would be the positive electrode and the $Cr^{3+}|Cr^{2+}$ electrode the negative electrode. The electrode reactions would therefore be

$$Fe^{3+} + e^- \rightarrow Fe^{2+}$$
$$Cr^{2+} \rightarrow Cr^{3+} + e^-$$

and the cell reaction

$$Fe^{3+} + Cr^{2+} \rightarrow Fe^{2+} + Cr^{3+}$$

The suggested reaction will therefore take place spontaneously.

(*ii*) Will iron(III) ion oxidize water to hydrogen peroxide in acid solution?

From table 13 we have the following redox potentials:

$$Fe^{3+} + e^- \rightarrow Fe^{2+}; E^\ominus = +0.771 \text{ V}$$
$$H_2O_2 + 2H^+ + 2e^- \rightarrow 2H_2O; E^\ominus = +1.776 \text{ V}$$

An argument similar to that used in example (*i*) above shows that in an appropriate galvanic cell the electrode reactions would be

$$H_2O_2 + 2H^+ + 2e^- \rightarrow 2H_2O$$

$$2Fe^{2+} \rightarrow 2Fe^{3+} + 2e^- \text{ (doubled to preserve the balance of electrons)}$$

and the cell reaction

$$H_2O_2 + 2H^+ + 2Fe^{2+} \rightarrow 2H_2O + 2Fe^{3+}$$

The suggested oxidation would therefore not take place.

Note. In example (*i*) the concentrations of the solutions were 1 M: it was therefore quite in order to use the standard redox potentials. In example (*ii*), however, no concentrations are quoted. Are the conclusions invalid for concentrations other than 1 M?

In fact if the Nernst equation is used to calculate the corresponding redox potentials over a wide range of concentrations it will be found that the magnitude of the potential of the hydrogen peroxide electrode is greater than that of the $Fe^{3+}|Fe^{2+}$ electrode in all solutions that would be likely to be met in practice.

Redox titrations

If a solution of an oxidizing agent is added gradually to a solution of an oxidizable substance the potential of a platinum electrode immersed in the latter changes during the course of the addition. This allows *redox titrations* to be carried out. Figure 35 shows how the potential of a platinum electrode changes as a solution of dichromate ion is added to a 0.1 M solution of iron(II) ion. The stoichiometric point is clearly detected by the rapid increase in electrode potential. Such titrations have some useful applications in analytical chemistry.

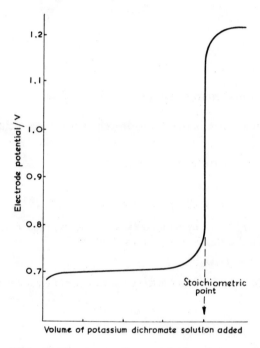

Figure 35 The change of potential of a platinum electrode in a solution containing iron(II) ions during the course of a titration with potassium dichromate solution.

Problem

Using the redox potentials of table 13, together with the potentials of table 11 where necessary, predict whether or not the following reactions will occur spontaneously in 1 M solutions:

(i) $Sn^{2+} + 2Fe^{3+} \rightarrow Sn^{4+} + 2Fe^{2+}$

(ii) $2Cr^{2+} + Cu^{2+} \rightarrow 2Cr^{3+} + Cu$

(iii) $2Cr^{2+} + Zn^{2+} \rightarrow 2Cr^{3+} + Zn$

(iv) $6Fe^{2+} + Cr_2O_7^{2-} + 14H^+ \rightarrow 6Fe^{3+} + 2Cr^{3+} + 7H_2O$

Irreversible Electrodes and Cells **10**

Polarization of electrodes

In previous chapters we have studied thermodynamically reversible cells and electrodes. Although, as was explained on page 53, a reversible cell is of great value in determining various important thermodynamic quantities, it has no use as a practical source of electric power. 'Working' cells are all irreversible to a greater or lesser extent and in this chapter we shall study the meaning and significance of this fact.

The reaction occurring in a galvanic cell takes place, in the absence of liquid junction effects, wholly at the electrode/electrolyte interfaces, the net cell reaction being the sum of two electrode reactions. In the case of electrodes operating reversibly the electrode potentials, as we have seen, result from a balance between two opposing processes, an *ionization reaction* and an *ion discharge reaction*. Under such circumstances the electrode potential is given by the Nernst equation for a single electrode.

However, in a galvanic cell through which a finite current is flowing this balance between ionization and ion discharge no longer exists. If a metal electrode dissolves at a finite rate in a solution of one of its salts the rate of ionization must be greater than the rate of ion discharge. If a metal plates out the rate of ion discharge must be greater than the rate of ionization. Accompanying these changes in rates there must also be changes in the potentials of the electrodes. To understand this let us return to a consideration of the Daniell cell.

If we connect the electrodes of this cell through some external circuit (say, an electric bell) electrons will travel round this circuit from the negative electrode to the positive electrode. Transferring electrons to the positive electrode will clearly reduce the positive potential of this electrode from its equilibrium value; similarly removing electrons from the negative electrode will reduce the negative potential of this electrode. The extent to which these potentials are reduced will depend on (*a*) the magnitude of the current flowing and (*b*) the extent to which the electrode reactions can compensate for this current flow. Although removing electrons from the zinc electrode will allow zinc ions to go into solution more readily (because the retarding effect of the negative potential has been reduced), even so this process will be slower than the rate of arrival of electrons. If the response of the electrode reaction is very sluggish, then, for a given current, there will be a large decrease in the magnitude of the potential of the electrode. Such an electrode can be described as behaving very *irreversibly*. If the response is very rapid then the degree of irreversibility will be small.

Conversely, if the natural flow of current in a Daniell cell is reversed by connecting it up to a sufficiently high external voltage, the potential of the positive electrode will become more positive, and that of the negative electrode more negative, than the corresponding reversible values.

Electrodes, the potentials of which have been shifted from their reversible values, are said to be *polarized* and the phenomenon is known as *polarization*.

Decomposition voltage

In order to reverse the natural flow of current through a Daniell cell, that is to bring about the reaction:

$$Cu + Zn^{2+} \rightarrow Cu^{2+} + Zn$$

the voltage *applied* to the cell must obviously be at least equal to the reversible e.m.f. of the cell. Because of the phenomenon of polarization it will in fact be greater than this.

It will be more instructive here to consider a simpler cell, one through which it is more natural to consider current being passed. The cell for the *electrolysis of water* consists simply of two electrodes (often platinum) dipping into acidified water. This is not a galvanic cell since it does not generate its own e.m.f. It might be expected therefore that, with no natural e.m.f. to overcome, any applied voltage however small would cause a current to flow and the electrolysis reaction to proceed. In fact, although initially the application of a small voltage causes a current to flow, this rapidly drops almost to zero. This is because the small current flowing leads to the liberation of hydrogen gas at the cathode and oxygen gas at the anode. The formerly inert electrodes are thereby converted into a hydrogen electrode and an oxygen electrode, that is we now have a galvanic cell with its own characteristic e.m.f.

This e.m.f. can be calculated by the application of the Nernst equation to the cell reaction. For a galvanic cell with hydrogen and oxygen electrodes the electrode reactions are

$$H_2 \rightarrow 2H^+ + 2e^-$$
$$H_2O + \tfrac{1}{2}O_2 + 2e^- \rightarrow 2OH^-$$

The cell reaction is the sum of these:

$$H_2 + \tfrac{1}{2}O_2 + H_2O \rightarrow 2H^+ + 2OH^-$$

If the cell is operating at atmospheric pressure $p_{H_2} = p_{O_2} = 1$ atm and the Nernst equation becomes

$$E = E^{\ominus} - \frac{2.303RT}{2F} \lg [H^+]^2[OH^-]^2$$

Now $[H^+][OH^-]$ is equal to the ionic product of water K_w where $K_w = [H^+][OH^-] = 1 \times 10^{-14}\,mol^2\,dm^{-6}$ at 25 °C. The equation then becomes

$$E = E^\ominus - \frac{2.303RT}{F}\,\lg K_w$$

(noting that $\lg K_w{}^2 = 2\,\lg K_w$). $E^\ominus$ for the cell is obtained from the standard electrode potentials for the hydrogen and oxygen electrodes. The former is zero by definition; the latter is obtained from table 11:

$$E^\ominus_{OH^-/O_2} = +0.40\ V$$

We then have

$$E = 0.40 - 0.059\,\lg(1 \times 10^{-14})$$
$$= 0.40 + 14 \times 0.059$$
$$= 1.23\ V$$

In practice, the minimum voltage which has to be applied to bring about the continuous electrolysis of water is approximately 1.7 V, that is about 0.5 V above the calculated value. This minimum applied voltage is known as the *decomposition voltage*. The difference between this and the calculated value is known as the *overvoltage* and results from the polarization of the electrodes:

decomposition voltage 1.7 V
reversible voltage   1.2 V
overvoltage   0.5 V

The apparatus for the measurement of overvoltage is shown in figure 36. A battery B is connected, through a variable resistance R and a

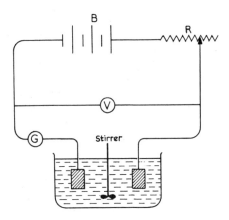

Figure 36 Apparatus for the determination of overvoltage.

galvanometer G, to the two electrodes of the cell under investigation. A voltmeter V across the electrodes measures the applied voltage. The resistance R is initially set at a high value so that the applied voltage is insufficient to produce continuous electrolysis. The resistance is then gradually reduced until electrolysis occurs as shown by the deflection of the galvanometer needle. A graph of current flowing against applied voltage has the form shown in figure 37. Extrapolation backwards of the portion CD to zero current gives the decomposition voltage at the point E_d: the difference between this and the value calculated from the Nernst equation is the overvoltage.

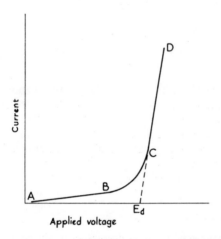

Figure 37 The variation of current with applied voltage for the system shown in figure 36. The decomposition voltage is given by E_d.

It will be seen in figure 37 that a very small current flows even before the decomposition voltage is reached (portion AB). There are two main reasons for this: (a) some current is necessary to charge the two electrodes (they have a certain electrical capacity and behave as the plates of an electrical condenser); (b) the products of electrolysis dissolve slowly in the liquid and diffuse away from the electrodes, some current being thereby necessary to maintain the layer of products at the electrodes.

Overpotentials

As we have seen, overvoltage results from the polarization of electrodes: this means that the cell reaction is not taking place reversibly. It is instructive to enquire further into the source of this irreversibility, to discover whether the two electrode reactions are equally irreversible or whether the irreversibility is predominantly due to one of the reactions.

This can be done by means of the apparatus shown in figure 38 which consists of two electrochemical cells with one electrode in common.

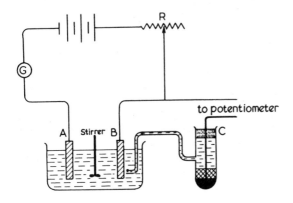

Figure 38 Apparatus for the determination of the overpotential of an electrode (B). The calomel electrode (C) has a different form from that shown in figure 33 but its behaviour is identical.

The left-hand cell (electrodes A and B) is connected up to an electrical circuit which enables the application of a variable voltage across the electrodes to be made, the current being measured on the galvanometer G.

The right-hand cell comprises the common electrode B together with a standard calomel electrode C, the side-arm of the latter being placed in close proximity to B. The e.m.f. of this cell can be measured by means of a potentiometer: since the potential of the calomel electrode is known (page 67) the 'working potential' of electrode B can be determined.

In order to carry out measurements the resistance R is set to such a value that a small current passes through the left-hand cell. As soon as this has settled down to a steady value the e.m.f. of the right-hand cell is measured and the working potential of B obtained. A series of measurements are then made of potentials of B for different values of the current flowing.

If, at a given current, the working potential is E', this will not be equal to the potential calculated for the electrode by means of the Nernst equation. If the Nernst potential is E then we can write

$$E' = E + \eta$$

where η is called the *overpotential* of the electrode. In a cell the sum of the overpotentials is equal to the overvoltage.

The overpotential is due to the irreversibility of the electrode reaction and this can have a variety of causes. As we have seen, the transfer of electrons to or from an electrode changes the potential of that electrode, the degree of change depending on the extent to which the electrode reaction can respond to the electron flow. Overpotential resulting from this cause is known as *activation overpotential*, because the rate of any chemical reaction depends on an *energy of activation*. For more detailed information on this the reader is referred to a textbook on chemical kinetics.

It is found that the magnitude of the activation overpotential of different electrodes varies considerably. The overpotential of the hydrogen/platinum electrode is generally very small whereas that of the oxygen/platinum electrode is large. In the cell for the electrolysis of water, therefore, almost the whole of the cell overvoltage is due to the oxygen overpotential.

There are, as well as activation overpotential, other forms of overpotential. *Concentration overpotential* arises whenever the reaction causes concentration changes to take place in the vicinity of the electrodes. If a current is passed through a cell consisting simply of two copper electrodes dipping into a solution of copper(II) sulphate, copper plates out on the cathode and goes into solution at the anode. In the vicinity of the cathode, therefore, the concentration of copper(II) ions decreases while in the vicinity of the anode it increases. This causes a change in the potential of each electrode. Concentration overpotential can often be eliminated by thorough stirring of the solution: in figure 38 a stirrer has been included in the left-hand cell for this purpose.

Ohmic overpotential arises whenever an electrode reaction causes changes in the resistance of the cell. When oxygen is evolved, for example, the electrode may be oxidized causing a thin film of oxide to form at the surface. This will have a high electrical resistance and so, to maintain a constant current, the potential must be increased.

For an electrode reaction at which these three forms of overpotential are present the total overpotential is given by

$$\eta = \eta_a + \eta_c + \eta_o$$

where η_a denotes the activation overpotential, η_c the concentration overpotential, and η_o the ohmic overpotential.

In studies of electrode reactions it is usual to avoid the occurrence of concentration and ohmic overpotential as far as possible. The activation overpotential, being related to the mechanism of the electrode reaction, is usually the one which is of greatest interest.

The exact relationship between the activation overpotential and the current flowing through the electrode depends on the mechanism of the reaction. In many cases the *Tafel equation* applies. This can be written:

$$\eta_a = a + b \lg i$$

where a and b are constants and i is the *current density*; this is the current divided by the surface area of the electrode. The Tafel equation has a similar significance for irreversible electrode reactions to that of the Nernst equation for reversible reactions.

Example

The overpotential of hydrogen evolution on polished platinum was determined at a current density of 1 mA cm^{-2} by measuring the e.m.f. of a cell comprising a platinum/hydrogen electrode in a solution of pH 3 combined with a saturated calomel electrode. The e.m.f. of the cell was found to be 0.660 V, the calomel being the positive electrode. What was the overpotential of the hydrogen electrode?

We first use the Nernst equation to calculate the reversible potential of the hydrogen electrode:

$$E = E^{\ominus} + 0.059 \lg [H_3O^+]$$
$$= 0 + 0.059 \times \lg 10^{-3}$$
$$= -0.177 \text{ V}$$

The working potential (E') of this electrode is obtained from the expression

$$E(\text{cell}) = E(\text{calomel}) - E'$$

or

$$E' = -0.416 \text{ V} \qquad (E(\text{calomel}) = 0.244 \text{ V})$$

The overpotential is given by

$$\eta = E' - E$$
$$= -0.416 - (-0.177)$$
$$= -0.239 \text{ V}$$

The Generation and Storage of Electric Power by Galvanic Cells 11

Modern civilization is dependent on the widespread availability of increasing quantities of power. Much of this is generated by the combustion of the fossil fuels, coal, gas, and oil, with hydroelectric and more recently nuclear sources making an appreciable contribution. Distribution is frequently in the form of electricity, all developed countries being served by widespread electrical networks from which power can be drawn as and when required. However, there are frequent occasions when a more mobile supply of electric power is needed and in these cases suitable galvanic cells can be used.

There are essentially two kinds of galvanic cell that can be used for the storage and supply of electricity: *primary cells* and *secondary cells*. In primary cells a chemical reaction, which can take place in one direction only, leads to the generation of electricity by such processes as were described in Chapter 7. In secondary cells the chemical reaction is reversible, allowing a *discharge phase* when chemical reaction leads to the generation of the required amount of electric power, and a *charging phase* when the processes are reversed. A primary cell can be discharged once only whereas a secondary cell can be repeatedly charged and discharged. A number of similar cells coupled to work in conjunction with each other is said to constitute a *battery*.

Primary cells

These are most commonly used in flashlamps, radios, and so on, when small portable sources of power are required. At the end of the life of a cell it is discarded. The power output of primary cells is comparatively low and they are therefore an expensive source of electricity. However, this is compensated for by their convenience.

One of the most commonly used cells is the Leclanché cell which consists of a zinc anode (which also comprises the container for the cell), a manganese dioxide cathode, and an electrolyte consisting of ammonium chloride solution. Due to hydrolysis the ammonium chloride solution is acidic:

$$NH_4^+ + H_2O \rightleftharpoons NH_3 + H_3O^+$$

and the following reactions can take place:

anode $\quad Zn \rightarrow Zn^{2+} + 2e^-$

cathode $\quad MnO_2 + H_3O^+ + e^- \rightarrow MnO(OH) + H_2O$

The overall reaction is

$$Zn + 2MnO_2 + 2H_3O^+ \rightarrow Zn^{2+} + 2H_2O + 2MnO(OH)$$

Because manganese dioxide is not a good electrical conductor the cathode is constructed from a fine mixture of manganese dioxide with about 10 to 15 per cent of carbon black. A carbon rod inserted into this mixture serves as a current collector and as the positive terminal for the cell.

To prevent spillage, the electrolyte is gelled by the addition of starch and flour. Such cells are known as *dry cells* although this name is rather misleading: if a cell were completely dry its electrical conductivity would be very low and it would not work. Substances present in the flour also help to prevent corrosion of the zinc and so extend the life of the cell. Zinc chloride is also added to the electrolyte: being hygroscopic this helps to reduce drying out of the electrolyte on prolonged storage.

The voltage generated in the Leclanché cell is about 1.6 V but, due to polarization, this drops to about 1.4 V when current is drawn from the cell. The voltage falls further if the cell is run continuously for some time due to the accumulation of zinc ions in the vicinity of the anode (concentration overpotential). However, on standing, the normal voltage is recovered as these zinc ions diffuse away into the bulk of the electrolyte.

With loss of hydronium ions the pH of the electrolyte gradually increases leading to the precipitation of zinc hydroxide on to the anode. This increases the internal resistance of the cell (ohmic overpotential), the performance of which therefore falls off. Eventually perforation of the zinc container may occur leading to leakage of electrolyte. Modern leak-proof batteries are contained in an outer steel container to eliminate this nuisance.

Various other forms of primary cells have been developed to give improved performance under a variety of running conditions. The *magnesium dry cell*, for example, is similar to the Leclanché cell but contains a magnesium anode instead of zinc. Magnesium has a standard electrode potential of -2.37 V compared with -0.76 V for zinc: this means that a higher voltage is generated. The lower density of magnesium means that for a given power output a lesser mass of metal is consumed.

In the *air cell* the cathode consists of porous carbon through which air diffuses to come into contact with the electrolyte, which is commonly alkaline. The anode is zinc. Because of the slowness of air diffusion, and hence of the cell reaction, air cells are suitable only for very low currents or for intermittent use. They have been used in hearing aids. The cell reaction is

$$2Zn + 2H_2O + O_2 \rightarrow 2Zn(OH)_2$$

The 'shelf life' of dry cells is limited because slow processes take place even when the cell is not used. To overcome this problem for special applications, *reserve cells* have been developed which are completely inert until activated for use. One such cell comprises a sheet magnesium anode and a copper(I) chloride cathode. The electrolyte is salt water which is only added, for example by immersion in the sea, when the cell is required for use. Batteries constructed from such cells can be used for sea rescue purposes.

Secondary cells

Primary cells can only be used until the reactant materials are used up or until polarization processes reduce the current output to an unacceptable level. It is not possible to regenerate the cells by reversing the flow of current. Although in the Leclanché cell the anode reaction is reversible, it is not possible, at the cathode, to regenerate MnO_2 from $MnO(OH)$.

When regeneration is desirable then a different class of cell is used, known as a *secondary cell*. Secondary cells can be charged and discharged many times before various irreversible processes render them too inefficient for further use.

The most important secondary cell is the lead/acid cell. A number of these cells together constitutes the lead/acid battery or *accumulator*. The anode is made of a spongy form of lead; the cathode is a lead/antimony alloy grid coated with lead dioxide; and the electrolyte is sulphuric acid of about 30 per cent concentration (density $= 1.220$ g cm^{-3} at 15 °C).

When current is drawn from the accumulator, lead dissolves at the anode, the lead(II) ions thereby forming insoluble lead(II) sulphate by reaction with the sulphuric acid:

$$Pb \rightarrow Pb^{2+} + 2e^-$$
$$Pb^{2+} + SO_4^{2-} \rightarrow PbSO_4$$

The overall anode reaction is the sum of these two reactions:

$$Pb + SO_4^{2-} \rightarrow PbSO_4 + 2e^-$$

At the cathode hydronium ions are discharged on to lead dioxide which is thereby reduced to lead(II) ions and water:

$$PbO_2 + 4H_3O^+ + 2e^- \rightarrow Pb^{2+} + 6H_2O$$

the lead(II) ions reacting, as at the anode, to form insoluble lead(II) sulphate:*

$$Pb^{2+} + SO_4^{2-} \rightarrow PbSO_4$$

The overall cathode reaction is therefore

$$PbO_2 + 4H_3O^+ + SO_4^{2-} + 2e^- \rightarrow PbSO_4 + 6H_2O$$

The total reaction, obtained by adding together the anode and cathode reactions, is

$$PbO_2 + Pb + 2H_2SO_4 \rightarrow 2PbSO_4 + 2H_2O$$

When the cell is charged all the above reactions are reversed, lead being deposited on to the anode and lead dioxide on to the cathode.† To summarize, therefore, the cell reactions for discharging and charging are

$$\text{anode} \quad Pb + SO_4^{2-} \underset{\text{charge}}{\overset{\text{discharge}}{\rightleftharpoons}} PbSO_4 + 2e^-$$

$$\text{cathode} \quad PbO_2 + 4H_3O^+ + SO_4^{2-} + 2e^- \underset{\text{charge}}{\overset{\text{discharge}}{\rightleftharpoons}} PbSO_4 + 6H_2O$$

$$\text{overall} \quad PbO_2 + Pb + 2H_2SO_4 \underset{\text{charge}}{\overset{\text{discharge}}{\rightleftharpoons}} 2PbSO_4 + 2H_2O$$

*Although lead(II) sulphate is formed at both electrodes this does not conflict with the requirement that a reduction shall take place at the cathode. In the form of the dioxide the lead is in the +4 oxidation state and the reduction is $Pb^{4+} + 2e^- \rightarrow Pb^{2+}$. At the anode the oxidation is $Pb \rightarrow Pb^{2+} + 2e^-$.

†Here we are using the terms anode and cathode as they apply to the cell when it is discharging.

During charging the deposited lead tends to form long crystals (dendrites) which, if they were to reach the opposite electrode, would cause short-circuiting of the cell. To prevent this, and also to prevent buckling of the rather soft lead plates, separators made of wood or porous plastic are placed between the plates.

From the equation for the overall reaction taking place in the cell it will be seen that during discharge sulphuric acid is used up, leading to a consequent drop in the density of the sulphuric acid. During charging the acid is regenerated with a consequent increase in the density of the electrolyte. The charge state of the cell can therefore be determined by means of a hydrometer.

A lead/acid cell should not be run to complete discharge. As the sulphuric acid concentration decreases the resistance of the cell increases, both because of the loss of electrolyte and because of the conversion of the plates to lead(II) sulphate which is a poor conductor: this leads to a considerable drop in the voltage of the cell. Also, lead(II) sulphate is a bulky material and the consequent expansion of the plates, if carried too far, can cause buckling and eventual disintegration. Charging should usually be carried out when the acid concentration has fallen to not less than about 50 per cent of its fully charged value. For an initial density of 1.22 g cm^{-3} this is a density of about 1.10 g cm^{-3}.

During charging the pH falls as acid is regenerated; when the hydrogen ion concentration is sufficiently high, electrolysis of water commences and gassing from the electrodes is observed. Further charging is wasteful and may lead to damage to the plates.

The voltage of a single, fully charged, lead/acid cell is approximately 2 V. In use this drops slightly at first but then remains almost constant until a fairly rapid drop indicates that recharging is necessary.

Fuel cells

Because of the loss of reactant, neither primary nor secondary cells are capable of continuous running. After a period of time the former have to be discarded and the latter have to be recharged. This is always a nuisance and in some applications it is a serious disadvantage. The *fuel cell* is a galvanic cell in which fresh supplies of reactants are supplied continuously to the electrodes so permitting uninterrupted operation. In the hydrogen fuel cell, for example, in which the overall reaction

$$2H_2 + O_2 \rightarrow 2H_2O$$

takes place galvanically, hydrogen and oxygen are supplied continuously to the anode and cathode respectively.

The Bacon cell (figure 39) consists of a nickel anode and a nickel/nickel oxide cathode with an electrolyte consisting of a concentrated potassium hydroxide solution. The electrodes are porous, the reactant gases diffus-

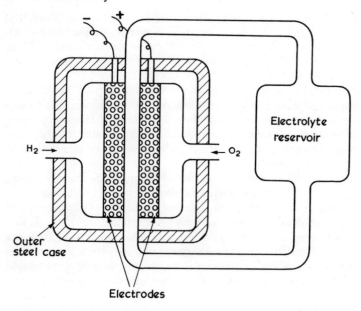

Figure 39 The Bacon fuel cell.

ing through them into contact with the electrolyte. At the anode the reaction (doubled) is

$$2H_2 + 4OH^- \rightarrow 4H_2O + 4e^-$$

and at the cathode

$$O_2 + 2H_2O + 4e^- \rightarrow 4OH^-$$

the overall cell reaction being

$$2H_2 + O_2 \rightarrow 2H_2O$$

Such a cell generates about 1 V.

Many different types of fuel cell have been developed in recent years. They are capable of much higher theoretical efficiency than conventional combustion based methods of generating energy and do not suffer the inherent problems of pollution or of the disposal of radioactive waste. The use of the H_2/O_2 cell in the Apollo moon flights demonstrated the capabilities of such devices but so far, with a few exceptions, fuel cells have not been put to significant commercial use. However, research is continuing as the potential benefits to mankind are great.

Industrial Electrochemistry 12

During the last hundred years industrial electrochemical processes have been of growing importance and have contributed greatly to the wealth of the more technologically advanced nations. Industrial applications are essentially of two kinds. Firstly, there are those in which electrochemical methods are used to break down chemical substances into simpler materials as, for example, in *electrodeposition* and *electrowinning*; secondly, there are those in which simpler materials are built up into more complex substances as in *electrochemical synthesis*. In all cases electrical energy is used to bring about some desired chemical change. In some cases electrochemical methods are the only ones that are practicable as, for example, in the electrolytic preparation of the highly electropositive metals from their salts; in other cases they may simply be more efficient or more economical, as in the electrochemical synthesis of a range of chemical compounds.

Electrodeposition

Electrodeposition methods are based essentially on Faraday's laws of electrolysis. In principle any element can be deposited at an electrode by a current being passed through a suitable combination of electrodes and electrolyte material. However, in practice many problems can arise and the development of electrodeposition techniques owes perhaps as much to accumulated empirical knowledge (the 'art' of electrodeposition) as to the scientific understanding of the principles involved. Passing a current through a solution of a salt of a metal can cause the metal to be deposited at the cathode but whether or not the metal deposit will be of any commercial value depends on a large number of variables many of which may be only imperfectly understood. In electroplating, where one metal is coated with another, usually for protective or decorative purposes, the deposit must be hard and coherent. However, if a current is passed through a solution of a simple metal salt the deposited metal will often have neither of these characteristics. It may well form a soft powdery or flaky deposit which easily rubs off and is of no commercial value. For decorative purposes a shiny deposit is often required but many deposits, even if hard and coherent, may be dull and unattractive in appearance. To obtain the desired results various additives may have to be included in the plating solution, the pH may have to be fixed, and the temperature of the solution and the current being passed carefully controlled. The metal on which the plating is being done may have to be subject to various cleaning and preparative processes, including sometimes the initial deposition of another metal.

Chromium plating

In chromium plating it is found that satisfactory deposits can be obtained, not from salts of chromium(III), but from solutions of chromic acid to which a small amount (about 1 per cent) of a catalyst (usually chromium(III) sulphate and fluosilicate) has been added. At room temperature the deposits are soft with poor adhesion but when the plating baths are heated a bright hard deposit is obtained. For decorative purposes the chromium is not plated directly on to the metal article: this is first given an undercoat of nickel or copper and nickel which improves the wear and corrosion resistance. Because the plating solution is acidic, hydrogen is evolved at the cathode while chromium plating is taking place. This does not affect the plating but it does reduce the current efficiency of the process.

As well as its decorative appearance, chromium plate appreciably improves durability and corrosion resistance and is widely used for tools and machinery.

Nickel plating

Nickel plating is another extremely important industrial process, more nickel being used for plating than any other metal. The composition of plating solutions can be quite complex depending on the particular application. A fairly simple solution consists of a mixture of nickel(II) sulphate and nickel(II) chloride together with a boric acid buffer and a wetting agent. This produces a good plate which resists wear and abrasion, even at high temperatures, and has many engineering applications. The pH of the bath must be carefully controlled. Above about pH 5 the deposits are rough and unsatisfactory due to precipitation of $Ni(OH)_2$ at the surface: below about pH 2.3 appreciable amounts of hydrogen are evolved which considerably reduces the current efficiency. The presence of the boric acid buffer helps to maintain the pH of the solution, although, in addition, small amounts of sulphuric acid have to be added regularly to the plating bath.

A great many proprietary additives are used in nickel-plating baths to produce different types of plate. 'Levellers' give a smooth surface on a relatively rough underlying material. 'Brighteners' produce mirror-like surfaces. Other additives can improve the strength, wear-resistance, temperature-resistance, and so on, of nickel plate and can be chosen to suit the particular application of the plated material. The mode of action of additives is often understood only imperfectly if at all. Many are organic compounds such as coumarin (a levelling agent) and saccharin (a brightening agent) and much research is being carried out with a view to developing an understanding of the nature of the processes involved and to help in the selection of new and improved additives.

Alloy electroplating

Many alloys can be plated from solutions containing salts of two metals and a few of these find commercial application, such as cobalt/nickel, lead/tin, brass, bronze, gold alloys, and so forth. These are often used for decorative purposes: for example, gold alloys in jewellery, and brass and bronze on hardware. Others have important engineering uses: for example, lead/tin alloys are used for coating ballbearings and cobalt/ nickel alloys are used on magnetic tapes.

Whether or not two metals will co-deposit depends principally on the values of their electrode potentials and overpotentials, that is, on the actual potentials at which the metals deposit. If the deposition potentials are close together (within about 0.2 V) co-deposition usually takes place readily. Sometimes metals which would not normally co-deposit because their potentials are too far apart can be made to co-deposit by adding substances which complex with the metal ions. For example, the potentials of copper and zinc are widely separated (+0.34 V and −0.76 V respectively) but addition of cyanide ion brings these sufficiently close to permit the electroplating of brass (a copper/zinc alloy).

Complexing agents are also often used in plating single metals for they can give much improved deposits with certain metals. Cyanide ion, for example, is used with copper, silver, gold, zinc, cadmium, and so on. The highly poisonous nature of cyanide means that special precautions have to be taken in handling the plating solutions.

Electrowinning

The ease with which a metal can be obtained from an ore depends principally on the position of the metal in the electrochemical series. The more noble metals may be found as native metal (for example gold and silver) or as ores which can be reduced to the metal by relatively simple methods. Reduction with carbon is possible with oxide ores of metals having electrode potentials more positive than about −0.5 V. Beyond this, carbon is ineffective although hydrogen may be a suitable reducing agent. However, for the very active metals, such as the alkali metals, magnesium and aluminium, such purely chemical methods are not applicable, and it was only after the chemical effects of electric currents had been discovered that these metals were isolated. The first metal to be produced electrolytically on an industrial scale was aluminium. Aqueous solutions of aluminium salts are unsuitable because electrolysis of these produces hydrogen in preference to aluminium. The electrolyte used is molten cryolite, sodium aluminium fluoride (Na_3AlF_3), to which is added alumina (Al_2O_3) and aluminium fluoride (AlF_3); these have the effect of lowering the melting point from about 2 000 °C down to about 1 000 °C or less, a considerable advantage of course from the point of view of production costs.

The anodes of the electrolysis cell are made of carbon; during electrolysis they are gradually oxidized to carbon dioxide by oxygen which is evolved there. The cell itself is made of steel with a carbon lining: this acts as the cathode, molten aluminium collecting at the bottom of the cell from whence it is siphoned off every day or two. Fresh alumina is added periodically so that the process is a continuous one until the cell lining is eventually worn through.

The electric current required for running an aluminium plant is of the order of about 100 000 A. For the process to be economical large supplies of cheap electricity are required and the location of aluminium plants is determined almost entirely by the availability of such supplies. Many plants have been built where cheap hydroelectric power is available, but natural gas has also been used for generating the electric power.

Alkali metals

The alkali metals sodium and potassium were discovered by the electrolysis of their hydroxides by Davy in 1807. The first commercial cell for the production of sodium came into operation in 1891 and used molten sodium hydroxide as the raw material (the Castner process), itself obtained from sodium chloride. Direct electrolysis of sodium chloride proved more difficult but a commercial method came into operation in 1925 (the Downs process). This is more efficient than the Castner process which is now obsolete. The electrolyte is a molten mixture of sodium chloride and calcium chloride, the mixture having an appreciably lower melting point (about 560 °C) than that of pure sodium chloride (800 °C). Chlorine is obtained at the anode and is a valuable by-product. At the cathode both calcium and sodium are formed (with about 5 per cent of calcium) though most of the calcium, being only slightly soluble, crystallizes out from the molten sodium as it cools.

All the alkali metals are produced electrolytically from their molten salts: other metals which are obtained in this way include magnesium, beryllium, calcium, and the lanthanides ('rare earths').

Copper

Metals which are less reactive can be obtained by electrolysis of aqueous solutions. Copper is one very important metal which can be so obtained. Although much ore is reduced to metal by smelting, about 10 per cent of commercial production is obtained by electrowinning. The ore is dissolved in sulphuric acid to give copper(II) sulphate solution and this is electrolysed using a pure copper cathode and an inert anode (often made of lead). The electrolysis reaction is

$$CuSO_4 + H_2O \rightarrow Cu + H_2SO_4 + \tfrac{1}{2}O_2$$

Sulphuric acid is therefore reformed and can be used for dissolving more ore. The purity of the copper produced in this way is 99.9 per cent or better.

The copper obtained by smelting techniques is very much less pure and is often refined electrolytically: this is known as *electrorefining*. The electrolyte is, as in electrowinning, a copper(II) sulphate/sulphuric acid mixture: the cathode is pure copper and the anode the impure copper which is to be refined. During electrolysis the anode dissolves and pure copper deposits on the cathode. Unlike the electrowinning reaction, which leads to the irreversible formation of oxygen, the electrorefining reaction is reversible, being simply the transfer of copper(II) ions from anode to cathode. Power consumption is therefore quite modest. The electrode potentials are such that metals more noble than copper do not go into solution at the anode but form a sludge in the tank, whereas metals which are less noble than copper go into solution but are not deposited at the cathode. The tank contents have therefore to be periodically purified to separate off these metals many of which are themselves valuable such as silver, gold, and the platinum metals.

Electrowinning techniques using aqueous electrolytes play an important part in the production of a number of other metals including cadmium, chromium, cobalt, manganese, and zinc; electrorefining techniques are important in the purification of gold, lead, nickel, silver, tin, titanium, and other metals.

The electrolysis of brine

The electrolysis of sodium chloride (brine) gives rise to the production of some important industrial chemicals. The electrolysis reaction is interesting because the nature of the products depends critically on the conditions under which the electrolysis is carried out. In *chlorine production* the anode and cathode reactions are kept physically separate. In 'diaphragm' cells this is achieved by keeping the anodes (made of titanium coated with a noble metal oxide) and the cathodes (made of steel) in compartments which are connected by porous diaphragms of asbestos. Brine flows continuously through these cells, chlorine being evolved in the anode compartments and caustic soda in the cathode compartments. However, the reactions are quite complex and a variety of impurities is produced. For example, hydroxide ion migrating through the diaphragm into the anode compartment reacts with chlorine to give hypochlorite and chlorate ions:

$$Cl_2 + 2OH^- \rightarrow Cl^- + OCl^- + H_2O$$
$$3OCl^- \rightarrow 2Cl^- + ClO_3^-$$

Some hydroxide ions discharge at the anode to give oxygen and to oxidize the graphite anode to carbon dioxide:

$$4OH^- + C \rightarrow CO_2 + 2H_2O + 4e^-$$

A number of organic impurities result from various reactions involving carbon, chlorine, and oxygen and in consequence only about 97 per cent of the current flowing through the anode gives rise to chlorine gas, the remainder producing various impurities and incidentally causing the anode material to slowly wear away. At the cathode hydrogen is evolved and sodium hydroxide produced, this process being almost 100 per cent efficient.

Another type of cell for the production of chlorine, the mercury cell, achieves the separation of the products of electrolysis by using a flowing mercury cathode. Although it might be expected that hydrogen would be evolved at this electrode, as in the diaphragm cell, this is not the case. The ability of sodium to form an amalgam with mercury causes the deposition potential of sodium to be reduced below that of hydrogen and consequently the principal reaction is the deposition and immediate amalgamation of sodium. The amalgam is reacted with water in a separate vessel to give sodium hydroxide and hydrogen: this is a galvanic reaction which takes place on the surface of graphite which acts as a short circuiting conductor between the water and the amalgam. This reaction is possible because the overpotential for the evolution of hydrogen on graphite is low whereas it is high for evolution on mercury. However, because of the damaging environmental effects of mercury, these cells are gradually being phased out.

In contrast to diaphragm and mercury cells in which the products of electrolysis are kept separate, in the *production of sodium chlorate* the products are deliberately kept in contact. Chlorine produced at the anodes dissolves in water and reacts with hydroxide ion produced at adjacent cathodes to give hypochlorite ion. When the operating temperature of the cell is above 30 °C the hypochlorite ion undergoes a further reaction to give chlorate:

$$3OCl^- \rightarrow 2Cl^- + ClO_3^-$$

The product therefore consists of a mixture of sodium chlorate and sodium chloride which are separated by crystallization.

At temperatures below 30 °C, and at higher pH values, reaction to chlorate does not take place and the resulting hypochlorite solutions are used domestically as disinfectants and bleaching agents.

Organic electrochemistry

An anode is, according to its definition, an electrode at which an oxidation reaction takes place. It could, therefore, be thought of as an actual oxidizing agent. Similarly, a cathode could be thought of as a reducing agent. The oxidizing and reducing abilities of electrodes can be controlled by varying the potentials applied to them: in consequence, they can be very versatile in promoting, in a strictly controllable fashion, a great variety of inorganic and organic reactions. We have considered above a few inorganic processes; many organic chemicals can be produced similarly, some of them on a sufficiently economical scale to be valuable industrially.

An important industrial organic reaction that can be carried out electrochemically is the production of adiponitrile:

$$\begin{array}{l} CH_2-CH_2-CN \\ | \\ CH_2-CH_2-CN \end{array}$$

this substance being one of the raw materials from which nylon is made. The usual chemical process takes place in several steps starting with adipic acid or 1,4-dichlorobut-2-ene. The electrochemical method is much simpler and consists of the reaction of two molecules of acrylonitrile to give one of adiponitrile:

$$2H_2C{=}CHCN + 2H_2O + 2\,e^- \rightarrow \begin{array}{l} CH_2-CH_2-CN \\ | \\ CH_2-CH_2-CN \end{array} + 2OH^-$$

The reaction occurs at sufficiently negative potentials at a mercury cathode, the high hydrogen overpotential of mercury meaning that the desired reaction takes place rather than the evolution of hydrogen gas. The acrylonitrile, which would not normally be soluble in water, is kept in solution by adding a substance known as a McKee salt.

Problems of solubility frequently arise when electrochemical methods are applied to organic synthesis since organic compounds are seldom soluble in water and their solutions in organic solvents seldom conduct electricity. McKee salts, which are salts of sulphonic acids, can overcome this problem and induce many otherwise insoluble substances to dissolve in water to give conducting solutions. They act in a similar way to detergents, the sulphonate anion attaching itself to the organic molecule and thereby bringing it into solution.

Another important electrochemical reaction is that for the production of lead alkyls which are used as anti-knocks for petrol. Production of lead tetramethyl and tetraethyl in the U.K. accounted for 54 400 tonnes of lead in 1973, although, with the increasing appreciation of the dangers of lead pollution, the permitted amounts are gradually being reduced.

One method uses as electrolyte a solution of ethyl magnesium chloride in an ether solvent. Ethyl magnesium chloride is one of an interesting and important class of substances known as Grignard reagents: these dissolve in organic solvents to give solutions which are electrically conducting as a result of the partial ionization of the reagent which can probably best be represented as

$$2C_2H_5MgCl \rightleftharpoons C_2H_5Mg^+ + C_2H_5MgCl_2^-$$

The anode consists of lead pellets and the cathode the stainless steel wall of the reaction vessel. At the anode the following reactions take place to give the tetra-alkyl:

$$4C_2H_5MgCl + Pb \rightarrow Pb(C_2H_5)_4 + 4MgCl^+ + 4e^-$$

$$4MgCl^+ + 4e^- \rightarrow 2Mg + 2MgCl_2$$

The solution contains an excess of chloromethane which reacts with the deposited magnesium to form more ethyl magnesium chloride.

$$Mg + C_2H_5Cl \rightarrow C_2H_5MgCl$$

This reaction also prevents the build up of magnesium metal on the cathode which would otherwise rapidly cause short-circuiting of the anode and cathode.

It cannot be claimed that organic electrochemistry is yet making a major contribution to the chemical manufacturing industry. Nevertheless, several important processes have been developed in recent years and appreciable research and development effort is being applied to this potentially most valuable field.

Corrosion

Although some metals (the coinage metals, the platinum metals, mercury) are found in the Earth's crust in a more or less pure state, many of those which are widely used industrially, such as iron, aluminium, and zinc, are normally found in combination with oxygen or other elements. These compounds are, in the oxidizing conditions existing on the Earth's surface, highly stable thermodynamically with respect to the pure metals. A consequence of this stability is that once a pure metal has been prepared it often exhibits a tendency, when exposed to an oxidizing atmosphere, to revert to the combined state, sometimes in fact to that of a compound resembling the natural ore.

This process is usually referred to as *metallic corrosion*. In the case of some important metals, notably iron, corrosion represents a major problem, vast sums of money being spent annually in attempts to prevent or minimize its effect.

The products of metallic corrosion are ionic in nature and corrosion mechanisms involve electron transfer. They may therefore be discussed in terms of the electrochemical concepts that have been introduced in earlier chapters. An understanding of corrosion mechanisms is very necessary if corrosion is to be effectively controlled: and there are clearly very strong economic reasons why this should be done.

Corrosion mechanisms

One example of corrosion that we have already met is given by the zinc electrode in the Daniell cell. When this cell discharges the zinc dissolves: we can say that in the cell environment the zinc corrodes to give zinc sulphate. The rate of this corrosion is limited by the rate at which electrons, produced in the oxidation reaction

$$Zn \rightarrow Zn^{2+} + 2e^-$$

are taken up by the reduction reaction occurring elsewhere. In the Daniell cell the reduction reaction is the deposition of copper:

$$Cu^{2+} + 2e^- \rightarrow Cu$$

In the absence of this, or some equivalent, reduction process, the corrosion of the zinc would not take place. However, as we well know, metallic corrosion can occur when a single metal is placed in a corrosive environment: for example, pure zinc in dilute acid. What reduction process could be involved here?

It is now considered that the surface of a corroding metal is divided up into, sometimes numerous, *anodic areas* and *cathodic areas*. On an anodic area of zinc the oxidation reaction

$$Zn \rightarrow Zn^{2+} + 2e^-$$

takes place; on a cathodic area a corresponding reduction reaction takes place. In dilute acid the most likely reduction reaction is:

$$2H^+ + 2e^- \rightarrow H_2$$

leading to the evolution of hydrogen gas.

But why should these different anodic and cathodic areas exist on the surface of the zinc? In the Daniell cell the two *different* metals are anodic and cathodic because of their different electrode potentials, the metal with the more positive potential being cathodic and the one with the more negative potential being anodic. It might be expected however that a single piece of zinc would be quite uniform in its properties. How, therefore, could the separate areas arise?

First, it should be appreciated that metals are seldom completely pure. If a very small amount of a more noble metal impurity were present then the atoms of this metal at the surface would constitute microscopic cathodic areas and these could be quite sufficient to permit a measurable rate of corrosion. If the impurity were copper and the dilute acid also contained copper ions then a whole series of microscopic Daniell cells could be envisaged on the surface of the metal. In confirmation of this mechanism we might note that zinc will dissolve much more readily in hydrochloric acid if a little copper sulphate solution is added.

However, even in the absence of more noble metal impurities, metals can still corrode, though the rate of corrosion may be less rapid. This can be for a variety of reasons, one important reason being that metal surfaces are not uniform when considered at the microscopic level. There will, for example, be different crystal faces exposed at different points at the surface and these different faces will have slightly different electrode potentials. We shall not normally be aware of these when we measure the electrode potential of a metal because we then determine an average value for the whole of the electrode. But in a corrosive environment these slight differences can give rise to the anodic and cathodic areas necessary for corrosion to proceed. Even strain in the metal can have the same effect, the potential of a strained area being slightly different from that of a surrounding unstrained area. Strains can arise for example where rivets pass through a metal and extensive corrosion in these areas may represent a serious hazard.

The corrosion of iron

Because of its widespread use as a constructional material the corrosion of iron warrants very detailed study and a great deal of scientific investigation has been carried out on it. As far as the anodic process is concerned this is:

$$Fe \rightarrow Fe^{2+} + 2e^-$$

For the cathodic process this could be the same as described for zinc if the iron were corroding in an acidic environment. But it is well known that iron will corrode under neutral or alkaline conditions and some other cathodic reaction must therefore be involved. It is easy to demonstrate that this reaction involves oxygen since iron will not corrode in water if oxygen is carefully excluded.

The cathodic reaction is

$$2H_2O + O_2 + 4e^- \rightarrow 4OH^-$$

giving rise to the formation of hydroxide ions. If, as is often the case, the anodic and cathodic areas of the corroding iron are in close proximity, iron(II) ions produced at the anode react with these hydroxide ions resulting in the precipitation of iron(II) hydroxide $Fe(OH)_2$. If sufficient oxygen is present further reactions are possible leading to the formation of a more complex substance of variable composition known generally as *rust*.

The Nernst equation for the cathodic reaction is

$$E = E^\ominus - \frac{RT}{zF} \ln \frac{[OH^-]^4}{[O_2]} \qquad (z = 4)$$

showing that the potential of a cathodic area is, in water, dependent on the concentration of dissolved oxygen. If, therefore, different areas are exposed to different concentrations of oxygen the oxygen-rich areas will be more cathodic than the oxygen-deficient areas. If a piece of iron is partially immersed in water the oxygen concentration will be greatest at the surface of the water: this area of the metal will therefore be cathodic to the submerged area, corrosion of which will then take place (figure 40).

Even the presence of solid particles lying on the surface of a completely submerged object can, by limiting the diffusion of more oxygen-rich water, give rise to localized corrosion cells.

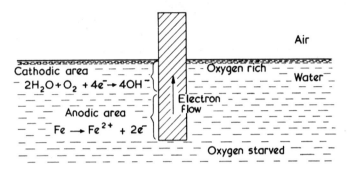

Figure 40 Anodic and cathodic areas on a piece of iron corroding in water. Corrosion takes place below the surface at the anodic (oxygen starved) areas.

The prevention of corrosion

The commonest way of preventing corrosion is to insulate the metal from the corroding atmosphere by a suitable coating such as paint. So long as the paint completely covers the surface, is not porous, and remains undamaged, corrosion will not occur. However, if moisture is able to penetrate to the metal this area will have access to oxygen: corrosion will then take place at adjacent anodic areas resulting in the flaking away of the paint and the exposure of more metal to the corroding atmosphere.

Alternatively, a metal coating can be applied such as chromium or zinc. The former is more appropriate for decorative purposes but zinc provides a very effective corrosion-resistant coating for iron, the process of application being known as *galvanizing*. A significant advantage of zinc is that if the coating becomes damaged the zinc, because of its more negative potential, corrodes in preference to the iron which thereby remains protected. Also the corrosion product $Zn(OH)_2$ usually seals the damaged area so halting the corrosion.

A third type of protective coating can be produced by reacting the metal with a suitable reagent. Oxide coatings, often resulting naturally from exposure of the metal to air, are sometimes sufficiently hard and coherent to protect from further atmospheric effect. Aluminium, which otherwise would be very reactive, is protected in this way. Iron, under suitable conditions, can acquire a protective oxide layer known as mill scale. Phosphating of the surface of iron by treatment with phosphoric acid can also be very effective.

Other methods of corrosion control rely on preventing either the anodic or the cathodic reaction from taking place by using substances known as *inhibitors*. Halting one of these reactions prevents the electron transfer processes which are essential for the continuance of the corrosion.

Anodic inhibitors include nitrites and chromates which are strong oxidizing agents. At the anodic areas, where metal cations are being formed, they bring about the precipitation of an oxide film which forms a hard coherent coating on the metal, so limiting further attack.

One significant characteristic of anodic inhibitors is that they can have

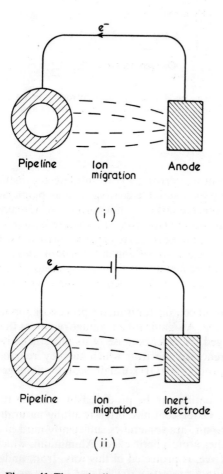

Figure 41 The cathodic protection of buried metal structures: (i) the structure is connected to a more active metal which is sacrificially corroded; (ii) an external battery impresses a negative potential on the structure.

some undesirable effects if used in insufficient amounts. If only some of the anodic areas are protected and if the corresponding cathodic process is not interfered with, corrosion may be intensified at the remaining anodic areas. The cathodic areas can still accept electrons at the same rate as before but these electrons will be generated over a much smaller total area. Consequently the actual rate of corrosion at the anodic areas may be much greater than before and this may well have serious consequences.

Cathodic inhibitors affect the cathodic process taking place and can be more generally effective. Hydrogen carbonate ion, for example, reacts with hydroxide ions produced at the cathodic areas to form a protective precipitate of carbonate which prevents the access of oxygen:

$$HCO_3^- + OH^- \rightarrow CO_3^{2-} + H_2O$$

However, if insufficient inhibitor is added to completely eliminate the cathodic reaction, the overall rate of electron uptake is reduced. This reduces the total rate of corrosion which, being spread over the same anodic area as before, is reduced uniformly.

Cathodic protection

A very interesting application of electrochemical principles is to be found in the cathodic protection of metals: this is used extensively for buried structures such as pipelines. Cathodic protection may be galvanic or it may depend on an applied polarization. In the galvanic protection of steel structures a more active metal such as zinc or magnesium is buried close to the structure to which it is connected by an electrical conductor (figure 41(i)). This metal forms the anode of a galvanic cell and is sacrificially corroded, the structure itself being thereby protected.

In polarization protection a cell is also established but in this case a battery is included in the circuit (figure 41(ii)). Hence the positive electrode can be any conducting material such as graphite, platinum, or scrap metal, the battery maintaining the structure at a sufficiently negative potential to prevent corrosion.

Further Reading

Books

Bockris, J. O'M. (1981) *Comprehensive Treatise of Electrochemistry* (Vols 1–4), Plenum Press.

Bockris, J. O'M. and Drazic, D. (1972) *Electrochemical Science*, Taylor and Francis.

Bockris, J. O'M. and Nagy, Z. (1974) *Electrochemistry for Ecologists*, Plenum Press.

Bockris, J. O'M. and Reddy, A. K. N. (1970) *Modern Electrochemistry* (2 volumes), MacDonald.

Covington, A. K. (1981) *Ion-selective Electrodes* (Audio-cassette + workbook), Royal Society of Chemistry.

Covington, A. K. (1984) *pH and its Measurement* (Audio-cassette + workbook), Royal Society of Chemistry.

Davies, C. W. (1967) *Electrochemistry*, Newnes.

Denaro, A. R. (1971) *Elementary Electrochemistry*, Butterworths.

Evans, U. R. (1981) *An Introduction to Metallic Corrosion* (3rd edition), Edward Arnold.

Hampel, C. A. (Ed.) (1964) *The Encyclopedia of Electrochemistry*, Van Nostrand-Reinhold.

Kortüm, G. (1965) *Treatise on Electrochemistry*, Elsevier.

Mathewson, D. J. (1971) *Electrochemistry*, Macmillan.

The Open University (1975) *Electrochemistry Parts 1 & 2*, Open University Press.

Potter, E. C. (1956) *Electrochemistry*, Cleaver-Hume Press.

Robbins, J. (1972) *Ions in Solution: An Introduction to Electrochemistry*, Oxford University Press.

West, J. M. (1971) *Electrodeposition and Corrosion Processes*, Van Nostrand-Reinhold.

Articles

Biegler, T. and Woods, R. (1973) 'The standard hydrogen electrode', *Journal of Chemical Education*, **50**, 604–605.
A discussion of the hypothetical nature of the standard hydrogen electrode and its true significance in the definition of electrode potentials.

Bockris, J. O'M. (1971) 'Overpotential', *Journal of Chemical Education*, **48**, 352–358.

Further Reading **105**

An historical review of the development of concepts of overpotential.

Childs, P. E. (1977, 78) 'Ion Selective Electrodes', Parts 1–3, *School Science Review*, **58**, 677–701; **59**, 88–99; **59**, 503–515.

Clever, H. Lawrence (1963) 'The hydrated hydronium ion', *Journal of Chemical Education*, **40**, 637–641.

Evidence for the existence of $H_9O_4^+$.

Conway, B. E. and Saloman, Mark (1967) 'Electrochemistry: its role in teaching physical chemistry', *Journal of Chemical Education*, **44**, 554–563.

The structure of electrochemistry and its relationship to other branches of physical chemistry.

Denaro, A. R. (1961) 'Electrode potential sign conventions' (Parts I and II), *School Science Review*, **42**, 389–396; **43**, 135–141.

A detailed account of the various sign conventions.

Denaro, A. R. (1968) 'Electrode processes', *Chemistry Student*, **2**, 40–45. (Reprinted in Stark, J. G. (Ed.) (1970) *Modern Chemistry*, Penguin Books.)

The origins of electrode potentials considered from the equilibrium and kinetic points of view.

Dickinson, T. and Ovenden, P. J. (1969) 'Electrochemistry in Britain', *Chemistry in Britain*, **5**, 260–264.

A survey of current electrochemical research and development.

Evans, U. R. (1967) 'The mechanism of rusting', *Quarterly Reviews*, **21**, 29–42.

An account of the mechanisms of the rusting of iron under a variety of atmospheric conditions.

Hawkins, M. D. (1973) 'Fuel cells', *Education in Chemistry*, **10**, 217–218.

Theoretical and practical aspects of fuel cells. Their advantages in relation to conventional power sources.

Huxley, J. V. (1973) 'Recent developments in copper production', *Education in Chemistry*, **10**, 94–97.

Describes present electrorefining and electrowinning techniques as well as other purely chemical methods for copper production.

Johnston, K. M. (1967–68) 'Organic electrochemistry' (Parts 1 and 2), *Education in Chemistry*, **4**, 299–303; **5**, 15–19.

Applications of electrochemistry to organic synthesis. Experimental methods, reaction mechanisms, applications.

Lawrence, Richard M. and Bowman, William H. (1971) 'Electrochemical cells for space power', *Journal of Chemical Education*, **48**, 359–361.

A description of some cells currently being used in space vehicles.

McIntosh, B. D. and Ridings, K. (1970) 'Inorganic redox titrations', *Education in Chemistry*, **7**, 238–240.

An outline of experimental potentiometric titration techniques.

Nicholls, D. (1967) 'Theories of acids and bases', *Chemistry Student*, **1**, 33–38. (Reprinted in Stark, J. G. (Ed.) (1970) *Modern Chemistry*, Penguin Books.)

The evolution of the various concepts of acids and bases.

Rechnitz, Garry A. (1983), 'Ion and Bio-Selective Membrane Electrodes', *Journal of Chemical Education*, **60**, 282–284.

Robson, Margaret and Wright, P. G. (1965) 'Equivalent and molar conductances', *Education in Chemistry*, **2**, 185–191.
Definitions of these and some related terms. A discussion of the relative merits of expressing conductances on the equivalent and molar scales.

Sammells, Anthony F. (1983) 'Fuel Cells and Electrochemical Energy Storage', *Journal of Chemical Education*, **60**, 320–324.

Sanderson, R. T. (1966) 'On the significance of electrode potentials', *Journal of Chemical Education*, **43**, 584–586.
The relationship of electrode potentials to energies of atomization, ionization, and hydration.

Sharpe, A. G. (1968) 'Oxidation and reduction', *Chemistry Student*, **2**, 16–19. (Reprinted in Stark, J. G. (Ed.) (1970) *Modern Chemistry*, Penguin Books.)
Oxidation and reduction discussed in terms of electrode potentials.

Siddons, J. C. (1964) 'Faraday's experiments in electrochemistry', *School Science Review*, **46**, 68–76.
An account of Faraday's methods, results, and conclusions.

Tingle, M. (1982) 'Membrane Cells for Brine Electrolysis', **64**, 50–55.

Venkatesh, S. and Tilak, B. V. (1983) 'Chlor-Alkali Technology', *Journal of Chemical Education*, **60**, 276–278.

Vijh, Ashok K. (1970) 'Electrochemical principles involved in a fuel cell', *Journal of Chemical Education*, **47**, 680–682.
A short review of the hydrogen–oxygen cell and some comments on other possible systems.

Wagenknecht, John N. (1983) 'Industrial Organic Electrosynthesis', *Journal of Chemical Education*, **60**, 271–273.

Williams, Iolo Wyn (1969) 'Batteries old and new', *Education in Chemistry*, **6**, 120–126.
The history of the electrical battery from Volta's pile to modern cells.

Young, I. G. (1973) 'Galvanic cells', *Education in Chemistry*, **10**, 166–168.
Describes an unambiguous procedure for the calculation of cell voltages and the deduction of cell reactions from electrode potentials.

Zuffanti, S. and Luder, W. F. (1972) 'Electron-repulsion theory: acidities of common acids', *Education in Chemistry*, **9**, 187–189.
A theoretical explanation of the variation in strengths of different common acids.

Index